# ALL THOSE BOTTLES

## ALCOHOL, I'M TELLING ON YOU

## Joseph McCray

# CONTENTS

Acknowledgments ................................................................. v

Introduction ..................................................................... vii

Chapter 1:  Alcohol Creeps In ............................................ 1

Chapter 2:  Alcohol Is Everywhere .................................... 7

Chapter 3:  Why People Drink ......................................... 15

Chapter 4:  Alcohol Is Deceptive ..................................... 23

Chapter 5:  I Think I Might Have a Problem ................... 31

Chapter 6:  Can I Continue to Drink? ............................. 49

Chapter 7:  The Effects of Alcohol .................................. 57

Chapter 8:  The Dangers of Alcohol Use Disorder .......... 79

Chapter 9:  I Heard There's a Way Out from Alcohol ..... 93

Chapter 10: What Happens If I Stop Drinking? .............. 99

Chapter 11: How to Stop ................................................ 111

# ACKNOWLEDGMENTS

I dedicate this book to my son, Goshen, who I pray will never taste alcohol or any drugs. Also, I dedicate this book to my wife, who helps me navigate this thing called life.

To my mother, who overcame alcohol and never touched it again in her life. You are my guiding light.

To my family and friends, who have helped make me who I am today.

Most importantly, to all the people and their loved ones who have to endure this challenge of an alcohol use disorder. May you find freedom within these pages.

And to my Lord and Savior, Jesus, who continually pushes me to be my best.

Wine is a mocker,
Strong drink is a brawler,
And whoever is led astray by it is not wise.
Proverbs 20:1 (New King James Version)

# INTRODUCTION

October 12, 2022. My wife, son, and I are here in Milwaukee, Wisconsin, with my family on vacation, and I think, this is the city of the most popular brand of alcohol. We go to the mansion of the great Frederick Pabst, one of the original founders of Pabst Blue Ribbon Beer. This was a town that thrived on making beer, which is still prevalent here.

I'm not a beer drinker, so I'm not interested, but what does strike me is the need to talk about alcohol in a way that makes you feel what I'm saying through these words. I hope to get you to feel my heart as I take you on this journey about my experience with alcohol, and may you think about it before drinking.

I know alcohol is widespread, and it isn't going anywhere. It will be a part of our culture long after this book is written, and many more like it.

# CHAPTER 1

## Alcohol Creeps In

I have so many questions to answer, but let me lay some foundation. I first experienced alcohol in my hometown of East Baltimore. I was born and raised a few blocks from the famous Johns Hopkins Hospital. There was a bar on the corner called Jimmy's. Jimmy would play music. You could hear the music from outside—the door would be open when the weather was good—and we kids would dance to the music. It was a sociable place, and it seemed OK. We were nosey. We wanted to see who was in the bar. We could look inside, but it was dark. You couldn't tell who was in there.

I believe most communities had a Jimmy's bar. We had a saying in Baltimore that there's a church on every corner and a bar on every corner. Both places gave something to the community, a way to deal with life when life got tough. Our neighborhood had the music and alcohol, and the music and the preached word about God, who is there to help us and see us safely through life.

I tend to believe that bars may have prevailed in the Black community, and I'd like to say they were the answer to the ills of my community; if you were feeling bad, you could

1

go to Jimmy's bar and get your drink on and forget about it all. You had your friends there. You had music, and you had a cold beer or a glass of a strong drink. The moment was short, but for that moment, the alcohol lifted your life. Your mind was relieved. You might even meet someone for the evening and rendezvous at their place and have an excellent time. It made for a variety of experiences in the local bar.

The local bar was the place to treat the spiritual, physical, social, and mental needs of the adults in the Black community. If you were depressed, you would have a drink; if you were stressed, you would have a drink; if it had been a hard day at the job, you would stop by and have a drink; if you just wanted to have a fun time, you would go and have a drink. If you wanted to feel like you belonged, you would stop and have a drink. Most of the neighbors stopped at Jimmy's bar. It was a big part of the neighborhood. Jimmy's was there to stay.

We had the church, but it would be later that the neighbors would go to the church. I didn't see many people going to church who went to Jimmy's on Fridays and Saturdays; they weren't getting up for church on Sundays, nor were the kids expected to go on Sundays. We did go to service at Easter, and for weddings and funerals.

Alcohol was not just at Jimmy's; it had moved up the street, and all those bottles had made their way into my house. How did those bottles make their way into my house? I'm still determining how, but they found their way into the house and brought the fun to my home. Seeing all those bottles of different sizes, colors, and shapes was amazing.

The bottles came out mostly around a card game called tonk. The jukebox would play, and there was so much joy and laughter in the house. Jimmy's had come to 2006 East Madison Street. We duplicated the Jimmy's experience. It was a weekend thing, you know. There was excitement, riveting voices that would get louder, and laughter, but sometimes they would go south, and that meant things would not be good. The people had changed. Something was in those bottles that changed them. They differed from the people they had been before they had those bottles on the table. Some were happy. Some were angry. Some people were crying.

As kids, we would be off in the corner wondering what was going on. What was happening? What would happen next? I didn't know alcohol changes who you are, and you are unaware of who you are while you are under the influence. The arguments and verbal disruption are what strike me the most. The uncertainty of what was happening. How could these bottles do this? I would cry. I cried many times and lost count of the pleas. And then my cries and wishes came true one day, and the drinking stopped.

The drinking stopped. We traded in Jimmy's bar for a church life. Change had come to 2006 East Madison Street. Our home had become a nonalcoholic home. Jimmy's was a thing of the past, and life was moving forward, or so I thought, but I had a curiosity and needed to explore life. I was interested in trying out this mixture. The one that had left me crying and pleading for its removal. Now I was introducing it into my life.

I had some great friends, guys who are genuine, and we are still connected today. I was the youngest of the group, and like a teenager, I was confused about what to do with my life. You're trying to figure out what you want to do, so you look to people who are doing exciting and fulfilling things, and you try those things. It's part of learning. I was no different. I remember it like it was yesterday.

It was Christmas Eve, 1982. I was sixteen years old. I was hanging out with my friends, as usual. We got together and played cards. We had some food, and we had some drinks. This Christmas Eve, I wanted to know what it was like to be drunk and what happens when you are intoxicated, so as my friends played cards, I was in the basement, drinking my beer and my Bacardi rum or strong whiskey. I drank it rapidly because I wanted it to work. It was my experiment, and I was going to learn what alcohol does. The next thing I remember is waking up on a sofa at my friend's home. I inquired about the sounds I could hear. It sounded like a washing machine was running.

I asked my best friend, Adrian, "What is that noise?"

"You need to shut up before I hit you upside your head," he told me, "because you vomited in my tennis shoes, and now they have to be washed and put in the dryer."

The first thing I did was deny it. I said to him, "No, I didn't do that," and he said, "Yes, you did."

I was ashamed. The last thing I remembered was drinking the beers and the Bacardi rum. I did not remember anything else. I found out a few days later that during this episode, my best friend had audiotaped me during what is called a blackout. Yeah, I had an alcohol blackout. An alcohol blackout happens when there is a rapid increase in the alcohol in a person's blood. When a person drinks about twice or more what they should over about two hours, it causes their alcohol level to double from .08 to .16. The person has no way to store new memories and becomes disinhibited; this is when they say and do things they wouldn't usually say and do, and they have no recollection of what they might have done. They're unaware it's happening because alcohol keeps the hypothalamus gland from storing new memories.[1]

That was me. I don't know that because I remember it but because my friends told me what I did. I heard the tape. The tape had a lot of laughter and the voice of a person with slurred speech. I made sexual comments about a young lady I fantasized about in high school. My voice described all the things I would do to her. The voice had no limits.

I was utterly at a loss for words.

I asked Adrian, "Who is that person?"

He declared with a firm voice, "It's you."

I was embarrassed. And this is what drunkenness looks like and feels like. You've become someone else, and you're not aware of the person, and those around you are unaware of who you have become. It was funny but pathetic. I had become a new person. It was not what I expected. I would never have believed my friends if they had just told me I said those things. But I heard it for myself.

Alcohol had changed me, and I had no recall. I could have harmed or been harmed by someone. It wasn't quite what I had hoped for when I had rapidly consumed alcohol. I wasn't sure what I was looking to happen. I wanted to know what it was like, and I did get my wish, not by my own means but thanks to a thoughtful friend who I credit with saving my life. I learned my lesson and never got drunk or intoxicated, blacked out, or passed out from alcohol again. I would go on to drink when I went to clubs or bars for the next few years. I did not stand out in the

---

[1]  NIAAA (n.d.). "Interrupted Memories: Alcohol-Induced Blackouts." Retrieved April 5, 2023, from https://www.niaaa.nih.gov/publications/ brochures-and-fact-sheets/interrupted-memories-alcohol-induced-blackouts#:~:text=Alcohol%2Drelated%20blackouts%20are%20 gaps,brain%20area%20called%20the%20hippocampus.

crowd and eventually gave it up entirely. I didn't need to prove anything to anyone; I was comfortable with who I was.

# CHAPTER 2

## Alcohol Is Everywhere

Sometimes I meet people who are frustrated that alcohol was even made. Why was this substance brought into our world? They think if we had never had it, then they wouldn't be facing the struggles they have in their lives. They're very serious when they say these things, and I, like them, wish alcohol had never existed at all.

- **Why was alcohol even made?**

I'm sure it was made to meet a need. We read about it in the Bible. It was made because it met a need—it soothes, it relaxes. Sometimes we hear the history of how alcohol was used for medicinal purposes. Sometimes they gave people alcohol just before they did surgery so they couldn't feel the pain.[2]

But nowadays it's made for mere recreational purposes, for the mere benefit of giving you a change in your life and

---

[2]   Keller, M., & Vaillant, G. (n.d.). *Alcohol and society: History of the use of alcohol.* Britannica.com. Retrieved April 6, 2023, from https://www. britannica.com/topic/alcohol-consumption/Alcohol-and-society.

how you feel and making the mood better or the meal taste better.

• **Why is there so much alcohol around?**

I think it's plentiful because there is demand for it. When you look at supply and demand, there are a lot of people who like alcohol—they love it—and there are so many varieties and so many choices, so many amounts, so many different tastes to pick from and choose what you want. It's a huge part of our culture, a huge part of our meals and festivities.

The grades and quality of alcohol vary. Sometimes alcohol can be very expensive—it's a huge tab to purchase alcohol—and the bottom line for the producers and sellers is just so high because it's so much in demand. We watch the Super Bowl and we see incredible commercials about beer. We laugh and chug along as we watch, but we know that behind the scenes, alcohol is destroying families, destroying communities, and costing the country hundreds of billions of dollars in lost productivity and medical costs. "The cost of excessive alcohol use in the US was almost a quarter trillion dollars in 2010."[3] But still, with so much demand, it's always going to be plentiful.

• **Why are bars and liquor stores so plentiful in my city?**

My patients ask me this sometimes: "Why are there so many liquor stores here in Baltimore?" I don't think Baltimore is any different than any other city. I think that you'd probably find the same number of bars in any urban

---

[3] Center for Disease Control (n.d.). *Alcohol and the Brain: An Overview.* www.cdc.gov/. Retrieved April 6, 2023, from https://www.cdc.gov/alcohol/features/excessive- drinking.html.

area. When I hear people say there are so many bars, I think this is an excuse they are using, because they want to say that if there weren't so many bars, if alcohol weren't so available, then they wouldn't have this problem. It just seems like no matter where they turn, there's a place to go and drink.

In any city, you will find bars and liquor stores because they meet a need, whether that's enjoyment, prevention of withdrawals or just not wanting to feel bad without alcohol. But the number of bars or liquor stores is not the issue. It doesn't matter how many bars are in this city or any city. It is a matter of deciding, what is your choice? What are you trying to accomplish? And if you're trying to accomplish sobriety, you're going to stay out of the bars. If there are ten in your area or if there are three, you just have no part in them because you know that going in there is to your detriment. It doesn't help you in your recovery or in the goals that you have for your life. That's my short and sweet of it. Your city is really no different than any other city, and what you do with the bars and liquor stores around you is your choice.

- **Alcohol is legal. Doesn't that mean it's OK to drink?**

When I give talks, I hear people say, "Well, alcohol is legal." And some people say it with disgust, I think because they wish that it wasn't legal. But people would still find a way to obtain it if it were illegal. In fact, it was once illegal, and we had a country still finding ways to get it illegally because it met a need; it satisfied something. There was a longing for it. People got some benefits, and they got their needs met when they used it illegally. If you want something, you will go to extremes to get it, no matter what it takes. And we see that all across life. If you want something, you'll drive long distances, pay incredible amounts of money, and spend tremendous amounts of time to obtain it. After a few years, our country went on and made alcohol legal again because they realized that despite all the problems with it, people wanted the substance and were finding ways to get it—sometimes in pretty dangerous ways.[4] Legalizing and regulating it, and letting people know the consumption amount and the percentage of alcohol in drinks, make it safer. And at the same time, we used the revenues to help the economy of the United States.

It's still no excuse to drink. Just because a liquor store is quite easily accessible doesn't mean you should go into that store. And it's no excuse to say, "Well, if I shouldn't drink, there shouldn't be so many liquor stores available. There shouldn't be such access to it."

Alcohol being legal is just not an excuse for you to drink. The fact that there are liquor stores right in your vicinity is not an excuse to drink. You, like many people, can ignore them. You can find ways to deal with the trigger of an alcohol store or bar, you can find ways to ignore it or take another route so you don't have to see it. If driving past that store is tempting, you can avoid it. So, enough of that excuse. It's time to be responsible and not continue in a behavior you know is not suitable for you.

- **Why are there commercials highlighting beers during the Super Bowl?**

This is an interesting phenomenon. As much as we say we don't want alcohol, we know alcohol is bad, a lot of our country does like alcohol. And we do like beer, and we look

---

[4]  Adrian, M. (2015). What the history of drugs can teach us about the current cannabis legalization process: Unfinished business. *Substance use & misuse*, 50(8–9), 990–1004.

forward to the beer commercials; they bring a lot of profit. They are associated with sports and activities that will always be part of our society, and we won't be able to push them away.

A group of people drinks for the sheer fun and entertainment of it, and that's it. They don't have unmanageable lives. They don't have health problems associated with it. They are not drinking and ignoring consequences that are happening to them. And so, because the masses outweigh the people who do struggle and do find alcohol causes their lives to be unmanageable, it is a popular item, and it generates a lot of money. And society is not going to turn down that profit because a substance affects a portion of the people in our country.

- **Why do famous people do beer and alcohol commercials?**

I do not understand this at all. Sometimes even athletes do alcohol commercials. I saw Serena Williams do a beer advertisement, and I thought, for an athlete, that just wasn't cool.[5] So, again, it all comes down to money. They have enough money that they can pick and choose what to do. I wish that they wouldn't do commercials about substance use, particularly alcohol. They probably wouldn't do a cigarette commercial, even though we don't see those anymore.

---

[5] The Sporting News (2023, February 12). Michelob Ultra Super Bowl commercial: Inside "Caddyshack" homage featuring Serena Williams, Tony Romo and more. https://www.sportingnews.com. Retrieved August 10, 2023, from https://www.sportingnews.com/us/nfl/news/michelob-ultra-super-bowl-commercial-caddyshack-serena-williams-tony-romo/xyakd4pqhsv6amhsthsgdgaz.

So this one is puzzling to me. I've seen the singer Usher doing alcohol commercials.[6] Also, P. Diddy or Puff Daddy, the rapper, is a co-owner of CÎROC vodka.[7] And I wish that they would choose something better to do. But again, the draw is they, too, probably take a drink here and there. And I think the advertisements draw people who genuinely don't need to drink alcohol.

- **Why do people cook with alcohol?**

People cook with alcohol because it's said to give the food a robust flavor. Typically, you cook the food enough to cook out the alcohol, leaving you with just the taste. I was told never to cook with wine that I wouldn't drink—I had a supervisor, Mr. Dell Uta, who shared that with me.

I'm told that there's not much alcohol in the food you cook with wine. But I tend not to cook with wine anyway. I know it may add some taste, but I'm just such an anti-alcohol guy that I don't even play around with that stuff. And when I go out to eat, I'm wary of ordering foods that are cooked in wine because maybe there's a little bit more content there than I would want. But people do it. People cook crabs in beer and things like that. It helps with the crabs.

I would say, if you have an alcohol use disorder or you're dealing with alcohol, I would just stay clear of it. I wouldn't

6    AdAge (2021, April 29). Usher and Remy Martin Explore the Ties Between Cognac, Music and American Black Culture N Stylish Brand Film. https://adage.com/. Retrieved August 10, 2023, from https://adage.com/creativity/work/remy-martin-team-excellence/2331596.

7    Cocktail DB (2023, June 13). Who Is the Owner of CÎROC Vodka? The Surprising Answer. https://cocktaildb.com. Retrieved August 10, 2023, from https://cocktaildb.com/who-is-the-owner-of-ciroc-vodka/#:~:text=C%C3%8EROC%20Vodka%20has%20become%20a,increase%20awareness%20and%20boost%20sales.

put myself in a place where I could be tempted or have a problem.

- **Do religious groups use alcohol in their ceremonies?**

Some do. Some use actual wine in Holy Communion, for example. But I believe that it should just be grape juice, because you never know who in a congregation might be struggling with alcohol use, and that wine in the ceremony could just be one more reason for them to conclude that, hey, it must be OK—after all, the church has alcohol in the Communion.

On another note, not long ago, I met Mr. Mark DeMoss, a public relations consultant for churches throughout the country. He shared that the two main reasons that Christian leaders fall from grace or compromise their integrity are committing infidelity with a woman and consuming alcohol.[8]

- **Why do people who are intoxicated get less harmed in an accident?**

The people who drink or get intoxicated and get in an accident are often not so badly harmed when the car crashes. That's because those people are limp. They aren't aware that the vehicle is about to crash into a wall or a tree. And so they don't tighten up or try to resist the impact.

If you're sober, when you see something coming, you put your hands up to try to avoid it. But when people are impaired, they're probably not going to move. Fear doesn't

---

[8] DeMoss, M. (2023, September 20). Finishing Well [Spiritual Talk]. Mark DeMoss.

rise in them because they are probably unaware that they are going to hit the tree or the wall. And so they don't respond. They don't tense up. They don't try to put their arms or feet out to withstand the impact. And so they're not as badly harmed as other people in the car who are not intoxicated.

# CHAPTER 3

# Why People Drink

I can't say why you started drinking, but I can answer it for myself, and I think a lot of people will identify with my answer—they saw alcohol in their homes, they got curious, and they made a decision to experiment. Or maybe they had friends who drank. I had both. I saw it as a child, and I had older friends who were drinking. And so, I had a couple of different exposures to give me an idea to want to try this. No, it just didn't pop into my head out of the sky. I was exposed to it. And I think a lot of people would say they were exposed to alcohol—they saw it somewhere, they hung out with somebody.

Some of you may read this and say, you know what? I just wanted to have a drink one day, out of the blue, and just wanted to try alcohol. Or you saw it in a movie and thought it was cool, or maybe somebody you dated drank. I don't know how you started drinking, but you know how you started drinking.

Genetics has a role in drinking as well. NIAAA says, "Research shows that genes are responsible for about half of the risk for AUD."[9] Genes are our chemical blueprint that determines what is passed along in our family, like blue eyes or being tall or short. It is believed today that an inclination to drink or attraction to alcohol can probably be passed on this way. The research says that genes carry 50% of the likelihood that people will resort to drinking alcohol.[10] The other 50% comes from our environment and the things we are exposed to, such as trauma, peer influence, parental examples, and curiosity.

- **Why do I drink alcohol?**

Why do you drink? Does it make you feel good? Does it keep you from feeling bad? Sometimes, people will drink because they've been drinking so long that withdrawals would begin if they were to stop.[11] They feel very bad when they don't drink. Sometimes people stay in addiction because they don't want go through that.

But there is a solution—we call it detox. Detox is a safe treatment in which the person is helped to slowly recover from the poisons that have been in their body, such as alcohol. We do it through medications called benzodiazepines. These are antianxiety medicines that mimic alcohol; they

---

[9] National Institute on Alcohol Abuse and Alcoholism (2008, November 4). *Genetics of Alcohol Use Disorder*. https://www.niaaa.nih.gov. Retrieved April 6, 2023, from https://www.niaaa.nih.gov/alcohols-effects-health/alcohol-use-disorder/genetics-alcohol-use-disorder.

[10] Ibid.

[11] National Institute on Alcohol Abuse and Alcoholism (n.d.). *The Cycle of Alcohol Addiction*. https://www.niaaa.nih.gov. Retrieved April 19, 2023, from https://www.niaaa.nih.gov/sites/default/files/publications/31954_NIAAA_The_Cycle_of_Alcohol_Addiction_v4_508.pdf.

have some of the same composition that alcohol has and have some of the same effects on the brain.[12] Using these medications, a person can safely taper off alcohol through detox. It can take several days, but we in the medical community have a lot of experience and we know how to help you stop drinking. So, you don't have to worry about feeling terrible if you stop. Just check yourself into a detox program if you worry you're going to feel bad or if you've tried it on your own and had withdrawal symptoms.

What are some other reasons you might drink? Maybe you drink because you're treating a mental illness. We call that self-medicating. Perhaps you're treating boredom, loneliness, and feelings that you might hurt yourself. Maybe you are dealing with depression, and you feel like drinking helps you through. Well, it is not an effective way to feel better. A more effective way might be to talk with someone and work through your problems or issues, and then it may be that, by talking and learning coping skills and how to deal with relationships, you may be able not to drink.

Maybe drinking is a replacement for medications you need for your brain to help you modulate an imbalance, like a significant depression or bipolar disorder. In bipolar disorder, you have highs, like a stimulant effect going on in your brain, and lows, like a depressant effect in the brain. But alcohol is not the treatment for those disorders. Being under the care of a medical provider is the way to treat them, or having a professional counselor to help you navigate through this.

---

[12] National Institute on Alcohol Abuse and Alcoholism (2022, May 6). *Alcohol Use Disorder: From Risk to Diagnosis to Recovery*. https://www.niaaa.nih.gov. Retrieved April 19, 2023, from https://www.niaaa.nih.gov/health-professionals-communities/core-resource-on-alcohol/alcohol-use-disorder-risk-diagnosis-recovery#pub-toc5.

You might simply drink like I used to, just to be accepted. You may not want to stand out or look odd in the club or at a social affair, so you get a drink to fit in.

I remember being there. I remember not wanting to be the odd man out, so I would get a beer, I would get a Löwenbräu beer and sip on it and hold it and talk with people. It took a while before I became comfortable with not drinking. When I would go out, alcohol was a huge part of that, and of socializing at parties. But because I loved to dance, and I learned that the alcohol would cause me to be off balance, I just eventually left it alone.

Or it might not be about big social gatherings for you—you may drink because your family drinks and everyone around you drinks. And that would mean you would have to change that environment.

Maybe stress drives you to drink. We all get stressed, we all get overwhelmed, we get to the point where we need something to relieve that, to make things better. Some people eat, some people go to the movies, some people play a game—and some people take a drink.

What else might drive you to drink? It could be it enhances your sex life or makes you feel confident hanging around your friends. There are many reasons. When I used to drink, I did it to fit in, to look the part. But only you know what drives you to drink.

So this is a question for you to answer. Why do you drink?

- **Could I be drinking because I struggle with my sexuality or identity?**

Do you struggle with who you are, your sexuality or your sexual or gender identity? Some people will read this and say: "Yeah, I do. I'm not happy." Others won't relate to this. But take a look and see if this is an area that causes you to drink because of some confusion, maybe some acceptance issues going on, or perhaps because you want to change your sex. Maybe it's not acceptable to your family for you to be outside the so-called sexual norm in society.

This comes down to some real soul-searching, some real coming to grips with the reality of how you want to live your life. Do you need a substance to give you confidence in your sexuality or identity? I don't think you should. I don't believe that having a drink should be in your story. It only worsens the situation if you struggle with your identity or with your sexuality and add alcohol to the mix. I believe instead you should find a support group and learn what you need to know to be accepted. I would suggest suspending the struggle, coming to grips, and getting some counseling.

It would be best if you had some sound direction for what to do, and there are so many support groups and opportunities to get help. And so don't seek it in a bottle, don't seek it in a drink. You will just get led the wrong way, and you will get even more twisted by not having a truly loving and supportive environment to help you navigate through your life as it relates to your sexuality or your identity. Alcohol doesn't care about your feelings; it doesn't care about your heart. It just wants to be consumed by you. Addiction wants you. It just wants to continue to be absorbed, to continue to have a place in your life.

Alcohol doesn't care about all the things that fall apart, all the tears and crying. It's a very, very selfish substance. All it wants is to dominate and take over. Sometimes, when you start out drinking, you will have control. But over time, it will slowly take control until you're not really making the decisions at all. It's making decisions for you, telling you to buy more of it, to spend more time with it. If you're dealing with sexuality and identity, you don't need one more complication. You don't need one more obstacle; you don't need one more challenge. You need a sound mind to make good decisions, and you need a supportive, loving environment to help you navigate this time in your life.

- **Could I be suffering from a mental illness and self-medicating by drinking to relieve my symptoms?**

Sometimes people have depression, bipolar disorder, schizophrenia or an anxiety disorder. They might not even know they have these conditions. They don't know what's going on in their brains. They don't understand why they feel this way, but they know one thing: When they drink alcohol, everything just seems to be better. Everything just seems to go away.

They don't have the worries. They don't have concerns. Their mood isn't low. And so, just as a result of being naive, sometimes they are unaware that they are using alcohol to address a mental illness. And sometimes it's been a lengthy mental illness. Sometimes it's been a severe mental illness. And how does a person discover that they're drinking to manage their mental illness?

A person stops drinking when they decide that the risk associated with it is greater than the benefits. And then, when the person has stopped drinking for several weeks, they can get an evaluation—an assessment to see if there is an underlying mental illness, an anxiety disorder, depression.

If you think this might be your situation, you will need to search for a professionally trained person to help you explore your life and ask you to be honest about what is going on. Maybe you're trying to bury something deeply that's painful or traumatic.

You might even be self-medicating for post-traumatic stress disorder. I've read stories of many people in the service drinking, and I've learned from speaking to veterans that a lot of them had PTSD, and how they dealt with that was drinking in bars. It's an incredible problem with veterans. We've gotten better over the years at identifying and treating this condition, but for many, many decades, alcohol was much more available than treatment and understanding, and many veterans have used it to meet a need from the trauma associated with war, the stress of having to take people's lives, and the stress of always being at risk of losing their own lives.

I'm not saying it's at all right to drink alcohol to treat your mental illness. I think it only exacerbates your mental illness, makes it worse. But you see yourself and you know you've got to do something. You can't just have all this trauma and all this pain and no way to find relief.

Relief will come with some therapy and medication—not with alcohol as a treatment for your mental illness.

- **I know I have PTSD, bipolar disorder or schizophrenia. Can drinking treat my illness?**

No. These mental illnesses don't respond well to alcohol. They respond well to medications, certain therapies and being a part of a community.

According to Very Well Mind, "The self-medication theory of addiction is based on the idea that people use substances, such as alcohol and drugs, or the effects of other addictive behaviors, such as eating or gambling, not to seek euphoria, but to relieve dysphoria or change an uncomfortable emotional state."[13]

No research supports the idea that alcohol helps with PTSD, bipolar disorder or schizophrenia. Still, people drink to deal with these things. Some of them do not know that they have a mental illness; some know but just feel that alcohol is the way to treat it.

It's not the way to treat it. Please get this. It's not the way to treat it. The way to treat it is with therapy, with medications, with groups and with community support. Those are better ways to treat these conditions.

---

[13] Very Well Mind (1, January 1). The Self-Medication Theory of Addiction. https://www.Verywellmind.com/The-Self-Medication-Theory-Of-Addiction. Retrieved September 21, 2023, from https://www.verywellmind.com/the-self-medication-theory-of-addiction-21933#:~:text=The%20self%2Dmedication%20theory%20of%20addiction%20is%20based%20on%20the,change%20an%20uncomfortable%20emotional%20state.

# CHAPTER 4

## Alcohol Is Deceptive

Sometimes drinking alcohol boosts people's egos and makes them feel more confident. That's because it's loosening their inhibitions, making them feel more relaxed and comfortable. They may feel like they can now express something they've been holding on to for a long time, or they can now do things they were fearful of doing.

When you drink, do you believe you can achieve more? Do you believe you're better at your job? Better in your family? Do you have more confidence? Because alcohol has changed your brain, it has made you feel more courageous. The "liquid courage" is released in your life.[14] And you feel like you can suddenly do what you need to do.

But can you achieve more in your life with alcohol? I think that's a fallacy. I think that's a lie. I believe that it gives you a false sense that you can achieve more, since you can achieve more in your life with just your regular mind. Why would you need a substance to enhance or alter your brain

---

[14] Cambridge Dictionary (n.d.). Liquid Courage. https://dictionary. cambridge.org. Retrieved May 11, 2023, from https://dictionary. cambridge.org/us/dictionary/english/liquid-courage.

performance to be your best? You weren't born drinking alcohol. You didn't go to high school, hopefully, drinking alcohol. So, why now have you reasoned that you need to have alcohol to achieve more in life? Alcohol is a trick.

Don't be tricked. Don't be fooled. Don't get caught up believing that you must start your day with a drink, that you have to be at parties or gatherings with a drink, that you have to have a drink when you go out to eat. I don't believe that you need to have a drink to achieve more in your life. I hope that you will also see the same.

- **Does alcohol give me liquid courage?**

*Liquid courage* is a term we use when people become very bold under the influence of alcohol—when people say and do things they wouldn't without alcohol, like curse you out or really tell you the honest truth about how they feel about you. And that kind of behavior is not fair. There's a reason we have inhibitions. There's a reason we don't say or do things that are just not appropriate or it's not the right time. But with a drink, you can lose all of that. And for that reason, I would say liquid courage is not good. People can get hurt by the words you say or the things you do.

- **I think I might be a better person because of alcohol.**

Are you better? Are you better at what you do? Are you a better school teacher, nurse, doctor, or environmental service worker? Are you a better parent or a better preacher because of alcohol? Addiction will fool you. It will convince you that you are better with alcohol, that you need alcohol. It wants you to continue to feed it. In the world of addiction, we have a saying: "Addiction is cunning, baffling, and insidious." Or some people replace "insidious" with "powerful."

Let's look at *cunning*; it's sneaky, sneaky. Are you a better person because of alcohol? If you believe that, then it has conned you. It is cunning. It is telling you, "Without me, you are nothing." But I am saying you are something; you are somebody without alcohol. You are the real deal. You are yourself. You're not a fake or an imposter. You don't have to believe the cunning lies of alcohol anymore. You can be your original self without alcohol.

Then, addiction is baffling, baffling. *Baffling* usually describes something you can't figure out, something that leaves you at a loss. You cannot wrap your head around it. Alcohol tricks you and makes you believe that you can't do without it. It physically attaches itself to your brain chemistry so that without it, you suffer. It makes your mind believe that this is your friend, that it is a part of you—how could you ever think about not having alcohol with you? Well, that's baffling. It has baffled you so much that you've lost things, and you can't even wrap your head around how. How did you lose this relationship? How did you lose this job that you were so skilled at? How could your children walk out of your life? How could your spouse leave you? You are baffled. You have no idea what has happened.

Next, addiction is insidious. *Insidious* is a word we use to describe cancers. They have an onset that doesn't give you a lot of warning, doesn't give you a lot of signs and symptoms—you don't know that your body has a growth outside or inside of it. Alcohol addiction is like this. It sneaks up on you while you are under the effects of alcohol; you are caught up in it and do not notice that it is sucking the very life out of you.

Another word we use for addiction is *powerful*. Alcohol is powerful. It meets a need. It makes you feel good. It makes the world seem like a better place. It allows you to treat your mental illness without going to a therapist or being accountable. Something as powerful as alcohol addiction has to be met with powerful responses, with new words to say to yourself, new approaches, a new support system, new information to tell yourself, because it has told you lies for years. It has told you things that you have now become convinced are true.

You're not a better person because of alcohol. You're not a designer's original. You're not who you're supposed to be because of alcohol. If you are a heavy drinker or a binge drinker, you are not your best.

And sadly, you find out all too late how you have lost and shortchanged yourself because of alcohol. Be the best you are without alcohol.

- **I think drinking helps me be a more successful student.**

This is talking to the students—hopefully not the high school students, but the college students. People who go to college are exposed to a lot of new people; they may be in a new town, and drinking might be the thing to do. And we know from research that some of the highest numbers for drinking in our country take place in college. "According to the 2021 National Survey on Drug Use and Health (NSDUH), 49.3% of full-time college students ages 18 to 22 drank alcohol in the past month. Of those, about 27.4% of students engaged in binge drinking during that same time frame."[15] Not everyone keeps drinking; they might do it for a season while they're in college. But some of them do go on to continue a life of drinking alcohol; it becomes a part of their lives.

Are you a more successful student because of alcohol? I wouldn't think you would be successful if you regularly take in a depressant like alcohol. It takes your brain into different areas, triggers different feelings and releases dopamine, which causes your mood to improve. It changes so many different chemical reactions in your brain; it's the one substance that gets in the brain and touches so many areas, according to Dr. Koop, the director of the NIAAA.

So I ask you again: Are you a more successful student? You can't judge that by yourself. You can look at your grades. You can ask your teachers. You can ask your peers. Does drinking fit you? Now some people are just brilliant, and no matter what, they come out on top. But is the alcohol making it difficult for people to want to be around you? Maybe your grades aren't impacted, but are you successful in sports, are you successful with relationships, are you successful just interacting with people? Do you get angry or want to fight? Are you too loosey-goosey? All those things must be considered when discussing a successful student.

- **When I go out, I have a drink to look like I belong in the club.**

Some people feel like having a drink makes them look like they belong, like they should be there. Taking a drink

15 National Institute on Alcoholism and Alcohol Abuse (2023). "Harmful and Underage College Drinking." Retrieved May 18, 2023, from https://www.niaaa.nih.gov/publications/brochures-and-fact-sheets/college-drinking.

makes them fit in and keeps everyone else from feeling uncomfortable with them there with a soda.

As you know, that was my story. But I came to learn that I didn't have to have a drink; I wasn't there for the people, I was there for myself, and if people wanted to judge me because I didn't have a beer as they had, then that was on them.

You have to come to a place where you can make up your mind that you're going out, you're going to the club, and it is solely for you. How do you benefit from it? It is your evening, this is your money, and you ought to have a good time. And you have to be around people who accept you for who you are, not because you are a robot and you do what they do.

So, ask yourself this question: Do you have to have a drink to look like you belong in the club when you go out? You belong in the club. You paid your money, you put your outfit on, and you're ready to have a good time. So, enjoy yourself and have a good time and be sober. Come home, know where you are, see what you've done that night at the club. Don't be so excessive with your drinking that you have a blackout and are not aware of what you said to people. And don't get taken advantage of or become a safety risk to yourself or others around you. Think about some of these things.

• **Jesus turned water into wine, so drinking must be OK, right?**

I believe some people reason that in the book of John, the second chapter talks about Jesus turning water into wine and therefore drinking can't be so bad. But with further study of that, we find that the water he turned to wine may have been mere grape juice (John 2). The Bible even makes mention of a strong drink. There were two types of wines in the Bible: fermented wine and unfermented wine. In Hebrew the word is *yayin*, and it means both unfermented and fermented wine.[16] The Greek word for wine, *oinos*, means both unfermented and fermented as well.[17]

And so, with further study, we find that not all wine was alcohol-based or fermented. But I say that if you are in the church or any religious organization and you struggle with alcohol, even if Jesus did turn water into wine and you believe the wine was alcoholic, let's take a look at your life. Is this wine, beer or other alcohol that you're drinking causing your life to become unmanageable, or causing you not to be as productive? Alcohol can make you not even be in your right mind, not to even understand the things of God, not to be able to be used as a disciple of God, right? The only things that should be in our minds are the mind of Christ, learning God's precepts, understanding God's laws and what he expects of us.

I ask you to evaluate honestly and ask yourself why you drink and attend church. Ask yourself: Why do I drink and try to serve the Lord? Is it difficult for me to serve the Lord and still drink alcohol? Have I put alcohol before God? Have I made it an idol? Have I made it more important than God himself? Please answer those questions. And then tell me what you have decided to do.

---

[16] The Kefar (2020, February 18). Wine Words in Hebrew. http://www. thekefar.com/. Retrieved May 19, 2023, from http://www.thekefar. com/wine-words-in-hebrew/.

[17] Jesus – God the Son (1, January 1). Wine in the New Testament. http://www.swartzentrover.com/. Retrieved May 19, 2023, from http://www.swartzentrover.com/cotor/Bible/Doctrines/Holiness/ Drugs%20&%20Alcohol/wine_in_the_new_testament.htm.

- **Am I lying to myself about the changes that alcohol has caused in me?**

It all comes back to denial. Are you lying to yourself? Has alcohol changed you? Has it changed your personality?[18] I've seen people's personalities change even when they haven't been drinking; they become callous, their nature is not as loving. So, be honest with yourself and look back to that man in the mirror, that woman in the mirror.

Are you being honest with yourself about the changes that alcohol has caused? Look at your whole life. We are holistic people. We're made of mind, body, soul, spirit. We have a social life, we have a work life, some of us have a spiritual life. We have family. We have all these different aspects of our lives. What role is alcohol playing and how is it affecting you in these particular roles? If you sat down and did an evaluation, maybe with someone who is close to you, someone you trust, and asked yourself what kind of effect is taking place with your health, what would be the answer? Your health encompasses many areas, not just your physical health but your mental health as well. What is alcohol doing to your mental health? Are you happy with life? Do you get pleasure out of the things that used to bring you happiness? You have to take the time to get honest and do the evaluation—you have to sit down and look at the ways drinking changes you.

---

[18] National Library of Medicine (2018, February 14). *Alcohol use and personality change in middle and older adulthood: Findings from the Health and Retirement Study.* https://www.ncbi.nlm.nih.gov. Retrieved May 18, 2023, from https://www.ncbi.nlm.nih.gov/pmc/articles/ PMC6054906/.

# CHAPTER 5

# I Think I Might Have a Problem

Sometimes people have an idea that their life is not as good as it could be. They ask themselves what could be causing the problem, but they don't want to believe that it might be their drinking. Of course alcohol is a part of the problem. It could be a small problem, a moderate problem or a very serious problem in their life, but at some point they will have to face the problem the alcohol is causing before it worsens.

• **What is an alcohol use disorder?**

I can tell you a little bit about that. It's the new terminology we use to reduce the stigma associated with calling people an alcoholic, a drunk, a wino—all those very derogatory terms. And so we say you have an alcohol use disorder, meaning that when you started using alcohol, it caused things to be out of order. It caused things first to be out of order in your brain, because the chemicals in your brain got all out of whack, and it caused you to have a tolerance. You needed to drink more to feel the effects of the alcohol. And when you drank a normal amount, you didn't get much of a buzz, much of an effect, and you didn't enjoy that. Another thing that defines an alcohol use disorder is that you have difficulty stopping. When you stop, you feel uncomfortable, and you find yourself having to drink again. You also feel like you need to drink to get your day started. Usually the people around you are uncomfortable with your drinking, may not feel safe, and may feel ashamed or embarrassed about your drinking.

If you have an alcohol use disorder, you may experience negative consequences as a result of drinking. Your health can decline. You can be unproductive in your position. It could be a safety risk on your job. If, despite all this, you still drink, we look at that as an addiction.

Here's what the National Institute on Alcohol Abuse and Alcoholism (NIAAA) has to say:

> Alcohol use disorder (AUD) is a medical condition characterized by an impaired ability to stop or control alcohol use despite adverse social, occupational, or health consequences. It encompasses the conditions that some people refer to as alcohol abuse, alcohol dependence, alcohol addiction, and the colloquial term, alcoholism. Considered a brain disorder, AUD can be mild, moderate, or severe. Lasting changes in the brain caused by alcohol misuse perpetuate AUD and make individuals vulnerable to relapse. The good news is that no matter how severe the problem may seem, evidence-based treatment with behavioral therapies, mutual-support groups, and/or medications can help people with AUD achieve and maintain recovery. According to a national

survey, 14.1 million adults ages 18 and older (5.6 percent of this age group) had AUD in 2019. Among youth, an estimated 414,000 adolescents ages 12–17 (1.7 percent of this age group) had AUD during this timeframe.[19]

• **What's a functioning alcoholic?**

Some people are in jobs that turn their heads to alcohol use, working for people who are unwilling to fire them because of their drinking. Their boss can smell the alcohol when they come to work, but they do a good job, and it would be hard to find someone with their qualities to replace them. So the employer tolerates it. Then the person comes home, and the family tolerates it too. And some people call that person a functioning addict or functioning alcoholic.

I personally don't like the term. If you say "functioning," do you mean "good functioning," "productive functioning," "positive functioning," or "tolerable functioning"? Often, the functioning is poor. But their employer needs them, and their family needs them, so everyone tolerates them; people put up with their antics and behavior while they are destroying their health and relationships. And people let it be because of the greater need to have the family survive, to have the family stay together.

So, I don't accept the idea of a functioning addict or alcoholic. It's a misnomer. How can you fail in one area but be acceptable in another? How can you say "functioning" and then say "addict" at the same time? To be addicted

---

[19] National Institute on Alcohol Abuse and Alcoholism (2020). Understanding Alcohol Use Disorder. Retrieved November 23, 2023, from https://www.niaaa.nih.gov/publications/brochures-and-fact-sheets/understanding-alcohol-use-disorder.

means you have lost control. To be addicted means you have impaired your ability to make decisions and manage your life. Addicted means that you do things despite the consequences to your health, consequences to your family, and consequences to society. And we call that functioning?

I would give that person a level of functioning—mild, moderate, or severe dysfunction. I think that's fair. Maybe they function enough to get by, but the functioning could have been better without the use of alcohol. Putting "functioning" and "addict" together is almost like saying "oil" and "water"; they're totally separate, they don't mix, they don't come together, and you'll see two different things.

Here are some questions to ask yourself to figure out whether you have a problem with drinking.

- **Has my work performance declined due to my drinking?**

You probably will not be the best judge of this; you probably need to ask your supervisor, and you'll need to be honest with yourself, because sometimes people are in denial that they have a problem. And they know that not working would be the most devastating thing that could ever happen to them, especially if they have a family.

You might want to deny that your work performance is declining, that you're not as productive as you used to be. But we do know that alcohol takes a considerable toll on the United States economy, and a lot of that is lost time and lost productivity in the workplace. "In 2010, alcohol misuse cost the United States $249 billion."[20] And so it's without a doubt that, yes, drinking does cause a decline in work performance. But I'm going to leave it to you really look honestly at whether this applies to you.

You do have to work and survive, but you don't have to drink. You can choose to get your drinking under control. Stop so that you're not in jeopardy of losing your job and losing your family, which will make the situation even worse; it could throw you into a depression and make you suffer even more at the hands of an addiction to alcohol.

- **Do I need to drink to get started with my day?**

If you get up in the morning and say, "Where's my drink?" then it's without question that something is happening in your brain. You're accustomed to having a drink when you wake up in the morning. Maybe it's a routine; maybe it's because when you're down in the night, you start to have withdrawals in your sleep. When you wake up, you feel what they call the willies—you feel uncomfortable, you feel shaky, and now you have to get a drink to take the shakes and the willies away.

So, now we know we have a situation. When you wake up, do you have cravings? Did you crave a drink, wake up and not even think about washing or eating? You felt you needed to get a drink in you because you're not right without it? If this is your story, if you're waking up for the day to get

---

[20] National Institute on Alcoholism and Alcohol Abuse (2023, January 1). Economic Burden of Alcohol Misuse in the United States. https://www.niaaa.nih.gov. Retrieved May 18, 2023, from https://www.niaaa.nih.gov/alcohols-effects-health/alcohol-topics/alcohol-facts-and-statistics/economic-burden-alcohol-misuse-united-states.

started and your body is yearning to drink, you're craving or have a withdrawal.

If you're starting your day with drinking, if you're feeling the willies in the morning, that's a clear sign that things have reached a problematic level for you. You'll have to go through the demanding requirements of a detox and not let this substance, alcohol, rule your day.

- **Do I drink in secret?**

This is a big sign of a problem. I've heard stories of people hiding their alcohol all around the house. When they go into a treatment program, their spouse finds all these alcohol bottles behind the sink and in the closet because they wanted to give the impression that they weren't drinking. They don't want to let people know their dark secret. Sometimes people wish to go on saying, "Everything is fine, this is my life, I'm going to live it the way I want to live it, and you don't have to know about it." But people do know about it. People see the inadequacies in a heavy drinker. They see the riskiness. They see the possibilities for harm. They know that you could be better. They see that interactions with you could be better if you did not consume alcohol.

Being secretive could be because of embarrassment; it could be that you can't just pull out your drink and drink it at the table and have everybody see it. And, in some ways, it's good to be secretive and not let your children see the bottles, see all those bottles. Still, they see it in your behavior. You may be detached; you may have stopped making time to be around. Maybe they see that they don't have the fun that they used to have with you anymore because either you are under the effects of alcohol or you are feeling bad from the withdrawal from alcohol, in an up-and-down seesaw effect for you. And so, even though you may be drinking secretively, your actions are being displayed for all to see. And it's no secret. People are aware. And eventually, people will figure it out.

And if they watch you closely, they may see withdrawals, such as your hands shaking and sweating when you don't have that drink; they'll see that physically, your body changes when you don't have the drink. What's in secret will come to light. It's an old saying, if you've heard it before: it will come to light.

• **Am I hiding my alcohol in the house because I'm afraid of being discovered?**

I can't tell you how often I hear about people hiding alcohol because they don't want others to know their secrets. They don't want their spouse, loved one or friend to see they are drinking.

So, they have this spy thing going on and this secret agent stuff going on. And it might be kind of thrilling or exciting—no one knows, I've got it tucked away, I'm the cleverest person. I see this as a falsehood. You're just lying to yourself. You are being sneaky and conniving, just like addiction is. And you're not fooling anyone. Even if people don't see where the alcohol is hidden, they can see your presentation, and they can see when you're under the influence; your speech, your movement, the things you may do or not do. And they also can see when you don't have a drink; they can likely see tremors, shakes and discomfort in you, especially if you are a daily drinker.

So, you're not fooling anybody. You're not as clever as you think you are. People are aware, and one day, they'll discover the alcohol. A bottle will be there because you can only hide addiction for so long; it will eventually come out in the open. So stop all the hiding. Stop all the denial and just come to grips with your situation. Say to yourself: "Hey, you know, I've got to work through this issue. I've got to work through this problem. I've got to figure out how to overcome this life challenge." Call it a challenge. Call it an obstacle to overcome, a mountain to get over, and put all your energy and strength into overcoming it, beating it and being successful. And I don't believe you'll regret one minute of the effort that you make to be alcohol-free.

- **Am I ashamed of what alcohol has done to me?**

Sometimes people are ashamed. When I run groups on depression, I often talk about shame versus guilt. Some people would like to put them in the same category, but they are two different things. Guilt is feeling bad about what you are doing or what you have done, while shame has to do with feeling bad about who you are.[21] Are you ashamed of what alcohol has done to you? Do you feel ashamed about who you have become, the person you are, as a result of drinking alcohol? Have you found yourself to be callous, hard, or mean? Have you found yourself to be loose or anything goes? Have you found yourself not being the best decision maker? Have you found yourself not being the best parent or child? Are you falling in your grades in your school? Are people disassociating with you because of what alcohol has done to you? Has alcohol changed your health? Do you find yourself with health problems that wouldn't have been your story if

---

[21] Very Well Mind (2021). Shame vs. Guilt. Retrieved November 23, 2023, from https://www.verywellmind.com/what-is-shame-425328#:~:text=You%20may%20sometimes%20confuse%20shame,a%20specific%20behavior%20or%20event.

you had not drunk—if you had not gotten ahold of alcohol and continued in the consumption of it? Are you ashamed?

Well, I come with good news. You don't have to be ashamed. You don't have to continue to feel bad about who you are. You can begin to take the steps to eradicate this substance from your life, divorce this friend, and say, "Goodbye to booze. I'm gone. I'm out of here. I will no longer feel ashamed of what you've done to me. I will look beyond my past and look toward a future without you." And that would be reasonable. That would be a good decision. That would make a whole lot of people happy. It would make writing this book worth it if you have decided not to be ashamed anymore of what alcohol has done to you, but instead you've decided to turn around. Just be willing.

You see the Alcoholics Anonymous philosophy. Alcoholics Anonymous (AA) says you have to have a willing desire not to drink. The only criterion to come to an AA meeting or even become a part of the group is to have a willing desire; you want not to drink. You don't have to come there without a drink, but you do have to go with the attitude of a willing desire not to drink. And from that desire, from that will, from that decision that you made, you will grow. And so, no more shame about what alcohol has done to you. It's just time to turn around. It's just time to repent. *Repent* means to change your way of thinking. Go in another direction. And so, I hope you get rid of your shame and decide to go toward sobriety.

• **Have I been ignoring the consequences of my drinking?**

Sometimes people have not thought about the consequences of their drinking. They've been ignoring what alcohol is doing to, first and foremost, their health, making them not as well as they ought to be. And being in a state of denial will not change your health status. Before people get to severe liver damage, they must have mild and then moderate liver damage. There are tests that can look at your liver and see if there's any damage. But suppose you don't get to the doctor regularly and have checkups and blood work done. You won't know that alcohol is changing your body.

Have you ignored the other consequences of your drinking? Have you overlooked that family has removed themselves from you? They don't come around you as much, they don't call, they'd rather not have you at the party or the gathering because they know you're going to get outside of yourself—you're not going to be the same human once enough alcohol gets in you.

Have you received a DUI or DWI, a citation for driving under the influence or driving while intoxicated, meaning that you have so much alcohol in your body that driving is unsafe for you and innocent people?

You are not in a drunken state all the time. There are times when you are sober, and in those moments, someone should tell you about your actions, about the people you have embarrassed. And those stories may not be so dreadful. Yeah, you can have a good time, you can dance, you can laugh and feel good. But there's a very thin line between how much alcohol will make you laugh and how much will make you intoxicated, unreasonable, very angry, disrupting rela-tionships and causing people not to trust you because of your actions and what alcohol is doing.

So, I want you to take a perfect moment to think about this. Has alcohol been causing consequences, even if they are mild, that you wouldn't want to happen in your life? Take a look at that and see if alcohol has caused some consequences in your life—hopefully they are not irreversible, but some may have been very impactful, some may leave a lasting impression. You know what the consequences are. Have you ignored those consequences?

Addiction is when you use despite the harm or consequences that the substance is causing. It is when you know that your life is out of control. But there's hope for you. And it's time to turn around.

- **Have I had near-death experiences that can teach me anything about drinking?**

Have there been times when you have almost died or when you have almost caused the death of someone else? Perhaps a traffic accident when you have gotten in a car and just driven at enormous speeds? I think of the great swimmer Michael Phelps, who came out of a casino in Baltimore and got on the highway doing around eighty miles an hour.[22] Lives were at stake. And this is a star athlete, one of the most decorated swimmers of our time, and alcohol almost changed his entire life. It could have caused his demise. It could have cost people who were innocently driving in the area their lives.

We know that drinking impairs judgment. Maybe Phelps never intended to drink so much. Who knows? But his ability to make reasonable decisions was affected. He may have just lost count of his drinking, or he may have felt con-

---

22 ABC 7 Eyewitness News (2014, December 19). Olympic swimmer Michael Phelps pleads guilty in Baltimore DUI charge. Www. Abc7chicago.com. Retrieved May 11, 2023, from https://abc7chicago.com/olympic-champion-swimmer-dui-michael-phelps-trial-drunken-driving/443689/#:~:text=Documents%20show%20that%20the%2029,legal%20limit%20to%20drive%20is%20.

fident, like he was OK, he's a multimillionaire, who was he going to call to say, "Hey, I don't think it's safe for me to drive"?

Michael Phelps did sober up. He made a turnaround, and there's been no more mention of that type of episode in his life.

The near-death experiences—have they taught you anything? I've heard stories of people who stopped drinking and thought they were managing things and then had a seizure.[23] They had a seizure from the withdrawals and had a car accident.

In those cases, it wasn't that they were under the influence at all, but they did not safely detox themselves. Do you know that even if you decrease the amount of alcohol that you've been drinking, if you've been drinking two pints a day and you start drinking a pint, or half a pint, the brain can say, "Hey, this is not what I'm accustomed to" and can put you at risk of withdrawals? One of those withdrawals is a seizure, a loss of control of your nervous system, and if you're driving, you're going to have an accident.

Several days without alcohol can place drinkers at risk of alcohol withdrawal seizures. Having a seizure is serious business and something to reflect on; if you have stopped drinking after being a heavy drinker, you need to monitor if you feel uncomfortable and anxious. If you start to feel that way, get to the nearest emergency room. If you're a heavy drinker, it's a wise practice to reach out to the nearest detox unit—google it—and say: "Hey, you know what, I've been drinking for years, I've been drinking a lot, and I would like to just bring myself in for detox." It's safe, and that way you

---

[23] Web MD (2021, November 26). What Is Alcohol Withdrawal? Www. Webmd.org. Retrieved May 18, 2023, from https://www.webmd.com/ mental-health/addiction/alcohol-withdrawal-symptoms-treatments.

don't have to worry about putting yourself and others at risk from severe withdrawals related to alcohol.

- **Has my drinking driven people away?**

Have people disassociated with you because they have found that you don't handle your drink? That's another denial issue; it is also an issue of accepting that people have separated from you, people are not in your circle anymore, and hopefully, you can recognize that. And some of these people were vital people, very good friends, but they watched a change in you and couldn't tolerate it anymore. They couldn't sit by and watch it anymore, and they noticed that you had become somebody they didn't know. And I say this so often: drinking and drugs change who you are to the point that you don't know who you are—and the people around you and who love you don't know who you are either.

Perhaps you have changed and driven people away because they aren't sure who you are. They can't do the things they used to do with you; they can't have the times they used to have with you because you're now in an impaired state. Sometimes when they want to hang out with you, you put yourself in unsafe situations, jeopardizing their lives.

You might find yourself isolated because your friends have stepped away. Maybe that's when you think about your friendships, about the value of your family, and decide to make a change, to turn around and put drinking behind you. You decide to try to reestablish those relationships, to get those people back in your corner. Sometimes this is what helps you make that decision.

- **Have I attracted people to my life because of my drinking?**

On the other hand, you may have formed a whole new group of people who just like hanging out with you because you do what they do. You drink; they drink. You swap stories about different and better drinks, and these are your drinking buddies, your drinking partners. Some say misery loves company. You can always find someone to follow you.

You can track people who do what you do, who won't accuse you, who won't blame you for drinking, who will see your drinking like their drinking. I've seen relationships where both people are drinking, and they see no wrong in it—what could be wrong if we do the same thing? But that can only make the situation worse because no one sees the wrong in it, no one considers the changes, and no one sees the impact because both people are engaging in self-destructive behavior.

In your moments of sobriety, your moments of clarity, I encourage you to think about where this is taking you. Where's this relationship taking you? Where's this person who's come into your life taking you? Is your life becoming even worse as a result of continuing to be around them and continuing to drink with them? Food for thought.

- **Do people around me tell me I need to quit?**

The people around you can see what you don't see. It would be wise to take their advice. They saw how you started and how things have progressed. When I had my blackout, I lost the ability to control myself. I lost the ability to stop myself. I was an absolute embarrassment. That type of experience will always stay with a person. But not everyone will have an audiotape or video of themselves doing all sorts of things under the influence of alcohol. If you can be honest and trust the people who care about you, believe what they say you do, take it to heart and take it seriously, then hopefully, you will want to quit alcohol as well.

- **Am I avoiding the doctor because I know alcohol has affected my health?**

Do you not want to go to the doctor because you know when they do the checkup, when they check your blood, they're going to get a sense that something is not right in your health? I remember the story of a young lady who went to the doctor, and they were doing blood tests on her liver. Her liver showed some damage, and the doctor kept asking her: "Are you drinking?" They'd done other tests, scans of her liver, and they couldn't figure out why they were seeing some liver damage. And finally, the doctor just decided that the patient wasn't being honest and that she could no longer care for her.

But it turns out that that woman was drinking, and she finally had to come to grips with it. The doctor knew that the patient was in treatment. She sent a letter to the counselor, saying: "Hey, I can't treat her anymore because she's not being honest about her drinking; I believe she's drinking." The woman finally was confronted and indeed she was drinking quite a lot—close to a case of beer daily. And I admire this doctor for being so brave, you know, to write that letter to confront that patient because her health was in jeopardy.

Don't ignore your doctor. Go check your health out, because things can turn around for you and you can have a longer life and better quality of life. In your times of clarity and sobriety, listen to the people around you and go and get your health checked.

- **Do I believe my drinking is fine because I only drink beer, not strong drinks?**

Sometimes I hear from patients who say that they only drink beer—they don't drink vodka or gin. They don't realize that beer is still alcohol and enough beers become like a gin or vodka. Those twelve-ounce beers become equivalent to half a pint or a pint of vodka if you drink enough of them. And this is an area where people tend to minimize. People say, "Well, I drink a very low-percentage alcoholic beverage." And they feel comfortable with that, but they drink twenty of those low-percentage alcoholic beverages. That adds up to a strong drink.

What I've seen in my over two decades of working in addiction treatment is that this is typical with alcohol use. It's always this minimizing: "I don't drink that much." People tell themselves that and they tell other people that, because they don't want to seem like they are this glutton. They don't want to seem like they're an over-drinker. They don't want to seem like they're doing a pint every day or half a gallon, because that's just so out of place. It would make them such an out-of-control person. Who drinks like that? So, they minimize it. The patients I take care of tend to think they drink so much less than they really do.

- **Am I in denial about my drinking?**

This is what it all comes down to. Could you be in denial? Could you be in a place where you haven't accepted that you have a drinking problem? There's a test, and it's called the CAGE.[24] The C stands for *cutting*—do you have trouble cutting down your drinking? If you say, "I'm going to drink four beers" and you drink half a case of beer, that's a yes.

The A stands for *annoyed*. Are people annoyed by your drinking? If you honestly asked the people around you and let them be honest with you, are they annoyed about your drinking?

The G stands for *guilt*. Do you feel guilty about what you've said or what you've done—or what people have told you you've said or done, if you were in a blackout? Do you feel guilty about it?

And then the E stands for *eye-opener*. Do you need a drink to get your day going? Is your day only complete if you have a drink?

*Denial* is a powerful word for many people with an alcohol use disorder. In my experience working in the field, many people with an alcohol use disorder are in denial, not accepting that they have a problem and that drinking has caused their lives to be unmanageable or has caused them to lose some level of control.

You may look at the person across the street and say, "I don't have a problem like him," or "I don't have a problem like her." Well, there are degrees of alcohol use disorder. A

---

[24] American Addictions Centers (2023). CAGE Questionnaire (4 Questions to Screen for Alcoholism). Retrieved November 23, 2023, from https://americanaddictioncenters.org/alcoholism-treatment/cage-questionnaire-assessment.

disorder can be mild, moderate, or severe.[25] Check yourself with the CAGE test and see if you fit any of those criteria.

Or maybe you don't have a problem; you're not in denial at all. You take a drink here and there, and it's just for the sole purpose of where you might be or what you might be doing. You're not a binge drinker.[26] You don't drink four to five drinks on a few days out of the week and get to a place where you are high or intoxicated. Maybe none of that applies to you. You may not have an alcohol use disorder, and this part of the book may not be speaking to you at all. You can look at this page and say, "You know what, he's not talking to me." And that may be fine.

But some people are in denial and have not accepted that their drinking has caused a level of mismanagement of their lives, mismanagement of their finances, mismanagement of their relationships, mismanagement of their productivity in the workplace, mismanagement of their health, that things have become unmanageable for them to some degree—that they would have a much better life, a much better outcome, if they did not have alcohol as part of their story.

[25] National Institute on Alcohol Abuse and Alcoholism (2022). *Alcohol Use Disorder: From Risk to Diagnosis to Recovery.* Retrieved April 19, 2023, from https://www.niaaa.nih.gov/health-professionals-communities/core-resource-on-alcohol/alcohol-use-disorder-risk-diagnosis-recovery#pub-toc5.

[26] National Institute on Alcohol Abuse and Alcoholism (2023). Understanding Binge Drinking. Retrieved November 23, 2023, from https://www.niaaa.nih.gov/publications/brochures-and-fact-sheets/binge-drinking.

# CHAPTER 6

# Can I Continue to Drink?

Somewhere in your life, you will have to answer this question: Is alcohol good for me?

Is it a stumbling block?

Can I do without it?

Do I need to drink to get myself going for the day?

Do I take a drink to calm down from the day's stresses?

Is my life better because of alcohol?

Let me add my two cents. Alcohol is pleasant to taste, but it has an element of toxicity, which changes how you feel because of the changes in your brain.[27] You have to be the judge. I know for me, when I used to drink alcohol at clubs, it was so I wouldn't stand out; I didn't want to be the only one without a drink. I know alcohol made me talk differently and disturbed my balance, which made it difficult for me to dance. I had to wait until my body processed it or burned it off before I could dance as I wanted.

---

[27] National Institute on Alcohol Abuse and Alcoholism (2022, November 30). Alcohol and the Brain: An Overview. https://www.niaaa.nih. gov. Retrieved April 6, 2023, from https://www.niaaa.nih.gov/sites/ default/files/publications/NIAAA_Alcohol_and_the%20Brain.pdf

Eventually, I got the nerve to say no. It didn't matter what people thought about my image. I was OK with drinking Coca-Cola or a Sprite for the evening. I was there to have a good time, and being a people pleaser was not my goal, so alcohol was not good for me. Plus, I'd had that experience of having a blackout as a teenager. I had more than one reason not to drink. It wasn't good for me or what I wanted to do. It just didn't fit.

You might not have an alcohol use disorder, and it might still be best.

• **Is it safe to drink as a teenager?**

Drinking before you're twenty-one is a trick. It is a way to make you think you're now this adult. This one concerns me for a couple of reasons. I drank before I was twenty-one. I drank to the point that I blacked out and could have lost my life. I drank, and I vomited. And I could have gagged on my vomit and just died because my body was limp due to that excessive amount of alcohol. I was sixteen or seventeen years old. Your brain is still developing at that age, and it's still developing at age twenty-one.[28] It may go on developing until age twenty-four or twenty-five for men, and a little younger for women because their brains mature a little faster.

So, don't drink. Don't drink at all, but especially don't drink while you are a teenager. Are you a grown-up just because you drink alcohol? Do you feel like an adult? What about responsibilities? What about securing a job or doing

---

[28] National Institute of Mental Health (2023, January 1). The Teen Brain: 7 Things to Know. www.nimh.nih.gov. Retrieved May 19, 2023, from https://www.nimh.nih.gov/health/publications/the-teen-brain-7-things-to-know#:~:text=Although%20the%20brain%20stops%20growing,the%20last%20parts%20to%20mature.

well in college or trade school, or being respectful to your parents and the people who love you? What about those things, if you want to feel grown-up, to be mature –what about accepting responsibility? Those are the things that I would say should make you feel grown-up—not drinking alcohol.

If you're a parent, share this with your child, your teenager, your big grown son, your young cousin, your nephew, your grown niece, your daughter. Please share this with them. It doesn't make you grown-up to drink alcohol, to sneak a drink because you're underage. It is not growing; you are being dishonest and not following the guidelines and rules. There's a reason why they say not to drink until you're twenty-one: because they want you to be able to make mature decisions. They want you to have a compass; they want your brain to have matured. So, the law is not to drink until you're twenty-one.

- **Why do teenagers go away to college and get into drinking?**

Drinking is prevalent in college. When teenagers leave home, they get exposed to alcohol and influenced by peers. And teenagers are finding themselves and developing into adults, so they are exploring. According to the 2021 NSDUH, 7.3% of full-time college students aged eighteen to twenty-two reported heavy alcohol use in the month before they were interviewed.

It takes a lot of utilizing those support systems and those protective factors that you've been raised in not to put yourself in harm's way and not to drink, not to use cigarettes, not to have sexual relations until you're married and not to have many different relationships. It takes a lot of holding on to the principles that you know. So, it comes down to what the protective factors are that are going to remind you and keep you from getting into some possibly dangerous situations. The fewer of those factors you have, and the more risk factors you have when you go to college, as far as limited upbringing, not being exposed to a sound positive spiritual environment or understanding of a higher power or the God of your belief, and not growing up raised with good sound wisdom and direction, the more likely you are to get caught up in some dangerous things.[29]

It helps to have a support system like positive family members, teachers, churches or religious associations. A key protective factor is having a caregiver who created a safe and positive relationship with you, one who practices nurturing parental skills. Families who have strong social support networks where caregivers were present and showed an interest can also be protective against alcohol abuse in college.[30]

- **Can I drink during pregnancy?**

If you are thinking about getting pregnant and you drink alcohol, stop alcohol now or stop thinking about pregnancy. The two don't mix. According to the NIAAA, "A developing baby is exposed to the same concentration of alcohol as the mother during pregnancy. There is no known safe amount of alcohol consumption for women who are pregnant, includ-

---

[29] Alcohol and Drug Foundation (1, January 1). Prevention strategies. https://community.adf.org.au. Retrieved September 21, 2023, from https://community.adf.org.au/get-started/prevention-strategies.

[30] Ibid.

ing early in pregnancy when a woman may not know that she is pregnant."[31]

So, if you are pregnant, you just have to stop. You can't cut down—you just have to stop consuming alcohol for the safety of your child. Just give it up.

Alcohol is discouraged because of these possible risks: "[It] is associated with an increased risk of miscarriage, stillbirth, prematurity and sudden infant death syndrome (SIDS), as well as fetal alcohol spectrum disorders (FASD)."[32]

- **I'm not hurting anybody. Can I continue to drink?**

You may not know that you're hurting anyone. You may be in denial. You may just not be aware. And if you give yourself some sobriety and ask the people close to you what they think about your drinking, they will probably honestly tell you the truth. The question is, will you accept it? As we've talked about, a big part of alcohol use disorder is denial—just not accepting that you have a problem, that your drinking is out of control, that it has caused your life to be unmanageable in some areas.

And that unmanageability can be mild, moderate or severe. You don't have to wait until it becomes severe. If it's mild or moderate, it is still worth making some decisions for your betterment. We don't need to wait until all the things in our lives fall apart—we can start making some changes when just a few things are falling apart, right? We don't have

---

[31] National Institute on Alcohol Abuse and Alcoholism (2022, August 1). Alcohol and Your Pregnancy. https://www.niaaa.nih.gov. Retrieved May 27, 2023, from https://www.niaaa.nih.gov/sites/default/files/publications/pregnancy.pdf

[32] Ibid.

to wait until, as they say, all hell breaks loose before we start making a change.

And so, if you are thinking that you're not hurting anybody and wondering if it's OK for you to continue to drink, I say: Start by looking at your work. Then start asking that question to your doctor and your family members and your children. Ask when you have a clear head and can honestly receive what they say. Get an overall assessment from all the people connected to you, and only ask this question in a moment of sobriety. You should not be under the influence for this conversation. And then listen to what they say, and do your best to take it to heart.

- **Is it OK to have my wine each evening before I go to bed?**

Some people have been told that a glass of wine helps mellow you out. It also helps with thinning your blood. Wine has some anticlotting factors and might help the heart. However, I would like to mention that this year the World Health Organization stated, "When it comes to alcohol consumption, there is no safe amount that does not affect health."[33]

If your life is manageable and you don't see your life being out of order, if you can be honest that all you drink is a glass of wine, that's considered an average drink. And just one of them a night is absolutely within the guidelines. It's OK.

---

[33] World Health Organization (2023, January 4). No level of alcohol consumption is safe for our health. https://www.who.int. Retrieved August 10, 2023, from https://www.who.int/europe/news/item/04-01-2023-no-level-of-alcohol-consumption-is-safe-for-our-health

I'm not going to tell you otherwise. I wouldn't tell people not to drink their one glass of wine. But don't try to use the "it helps with my heart" line.

# CHAPTER 7

# The Effects of Alcohol

A lcohol has so many different effects—on you, on your
work life, your social life, your family and everyone
around you. I can't say enough about the effects of alcohol, but I will try my best to include as much as possible to
get you thinking about the risks of alcohol versus the benefits of alcohol use. I don't want you to look back over your
life and echo the age-old words, "I wish … I should've … I
could've …" At that point it's too late. Now is the time to
make the change for a better life.

## Effects on You

- **Am I honest with myself about what alcohol is doing
  to my life?**

Has your health changed because of alcohol? Have your
finances changed? Has your relationship changed? Has your
productivity at work changed?

Michael Jackson wrote a song that said, "I'm starting with the man in the mirror. I'm asking him to change his ways." Look in the mirror; perhaps you are like Michael Jackson. You may need to make that change. Will you be honest and make a change for the better? You're the only person who can answer this question now, for you, for your health. We only get one body; if we take care of it, that body will perform better.

It's common knowledge that alcohol can change your health.[34] It is a toxic substance, depending on the amount consumed. The good news is that our liver recognizes it and attempts to metabolize or break it down into a safer product and get it out of the body. But, in breaking it down, some damage occurs to the liver. More good news is that the liver is the only organ that regenerates—so it takes some damage, it does some restoring. But the more you drink, the more damage takes place, and the damage can progress faster than the regeneration.[35]

Drinking doesn't just affect your health. Your finances will change too. You will find yourself spending money to obtain alcohol. The money you waste will vary based on your taste—some drinks cost more than others. You could also be wasting time. The time to obtain alcohol, the time consuming it, and the time under the effects of alcohol are all time

---

[34] National Institute on Alcohol Abuse and Alcoholism (n.d.). *Alcohol's Effects on the Body*. https://www.niaaa.nih.gov. Retrieved April 13, 2023, from https://www.niaaa.nih.gov/alcohols-effects-health/alcohols-effects-body.

[35] National Institute on Alcohol Abuse and Alcoholism (2023, February 10). *Closing the treatment gap for alcohol-associated liver disease*. https://www.niaaa.nih.gov. Retrieved April 13, 2023, from https://www.niaaa.nih.gov/news-events/research-update/closing-treatment-gap-alcohol-associated-liver-disease.

wasted. You can waste so much time indulging in alcohol use.

I spoke to a guy who said he gets the urge to drink when he's bored. And as long as he's not bored, he's fine. That can be challenging, because how does he keep himself from getting bored? He might not know that boredom can be a sign of being depressed. Sometimes when people can't describe their feelings of depression, they use words like *bored, tired, lonely,* and *down* to explain their low state of being. Could this person be drinking to manage depression? Who knows. It would take further exploring on his part, if he wanted to be honest with himself. He might need to seek out help to find out why he is bored.

Another place to examine your honesty with yourself is in your assessment of how much you drink. Some of the people I have encountered tend to minimize their drinking. The four beers they actually drank become two beers reported. One pint drank is half a pint reported. I'm not sure if alcohol impairs their judgment and they don't remember, or they're ashamed to admit the real amount they drink. Nevertheless, getting honest about this may take some time. There may be a process to go through before a person can accept the reality that they have a drinking problem and they need help.

- **What is my drinking doing to my brain?**

Well, drinking does a couple of things to the brain. It slows down brain activity. It causes the brain not to function as it should. It acts as a depressant.[36] You see it in the slowing

---

[36] National Institute on Alcohol Abuse and Alcoholism (2022, May 6). *Neuroscience: The Brain in Addiction and Recovery.* https://www.niaaa. nih.gov. Retrieved April 19, 2023, from https://www.niaaa.nih.gov/sites/ default/files/publications/NIAAA_Make_a_Difference_English_1.pdf.

of your speech, the slowing of your activities, the slowing of your thoughts. It also impacts your judgment and your ability to make reasonable decisions. You may decide to go somewhere or do something when you're not in the right state of mind, depending on how much you've had to drink. It affects the chemicals or neurotransmitters that cause you to be more relaxed, and, in that more relaxed state, you may find yourself accident-prone, unstable with your gait, or less able to walk and stand.[37] And if you drink alcohol rapidly and reach a blackout, you won't retain new memories, and you may say or do things that you wouldn't usually say or do because your brain has gone into a place where you're not aware of what you're doing or saying.

I've heard stories of people in a blackout driving to other states and not knowing how they got there. I've seen people in a blackout get into fights they don't recall the next day.

Sometimes, you can consume so much alcohol that you develop alcohol poisoning. This is when your blood alcohol level goes up to 0.40, putting you in danger of having brain collapse; your brain can't function with that much alcohol inside it. This can kill you.[38]

There's so much that drinking can do to your brain. You may be thinking, "But I feel good when I drink. I'm able to talk to the young ladies," or, "It helps me go up and introduce myself to a guy who catches my eye." I met a man once who said he couldn't talk to women until he'd had a drink. He got what we call liquid courage. He started to feel bold and at ease. He didn't have any reservations, and he

---

[37] Ibid.

[38] National Institute on Alcohol Abuse and Alcoholism (1, January 1). *Understanding the Dangers of Alcohol Overdose.* https://www.niaaa.nih. gov. Retrieved April 19, 2023, from https://www.niaaa.nih.gov/sites/ default/files/publications/NIAAA_Make_a_Difference_English_1.pdf.

would talk to women. He was able to make a connection because alcohol had given him the boost to do that. But it's an inadequacy to need a drink to share your feelings about an individual, and there are ways to build the coping skills to be able to talk to the young lady or young man of your liking without drinking.

Alcohol does so much to the brain. Dr. Koob, the director of the NIAAA, told me that alcohol is the only substance that does so many things to the brain. Other drugs focus on certain areas of the brain, but alcohol touches on just about every aspect of the brain. Above all, it affects the areas of the brain that control balance, the areas that control our decision-making, and the frontal lobe.[39]

- **What does my drinking do to my mind?**

Some say the mind is separate from the brain; the mind is your emotions, your inner self.[40] And drinking does something to your mind. It causes the mind to feel a sense of satisfaction or belonging from drinking, and to feel that drinking fits into your life emotionally—that your life is much better because of alcohol.

I want you to explore what drinking is doing to your mind. What is it doing to your inner self, your inner being? How is it making you feel as a person? Do you feel like you are adequate with it or without it? What is your emotional state while you are under the influence of alcohol? Do you

---

[39] YouTube (2021, April 1). What is the Neurobiology of Addiction? Dr. George Koob Interview. https://www.youtube.com. Retrieved April 19, 2023, from https://youtu.be/ev1vb6X175U.

[40] Psychology Today (2011). What Is the Mind? Retrieved November 23, 2023, from https://www.psychologytoday.com/us/blog/theory-knowledge/201112/what-is-the-mind.

feel like you count? Like you belong? Do you see alcohol as a friend? Do you think that if you didn't have it, you would feel friendless, alone, like a part of you had been taken away?

So, ask yourself: What is my drinking doing to my mind? What is my drinking doing to my social life? Do I even have a social life without a drink? Some people who drink are very lonely or isolated. Maybe their drinking is very private; they're in the comfort of their home when they drink. But then some go out and maybe have dinner or go to a club, and they bring their drink along with them; they're the friendliest person at the party, the life of the party, but it is with the assistance of alcohol.

- **Can drinking change my personality?**

After years of drinking, you begin to form another personality. You begin to change your own understanding of who you know yourself to be, because your characteristics and behaviors have changed. You begin to deal with the guilt and the shame of alcohol. You begin to deal with the denial of alcohol and the cover-up and making it seem like nothing is really wrong with you, like you've really got it together. That's a persona that you're trying to project to people that isn't really true.

It's actually deception. It is deceptive because you want people to see you as OK, because to be intoxicated and out of control is embarrassing. And so, your personality has to change. The person you are has to change and become something else.

Does alcohol change a person's personality? I believe it does. I've seen people become another person—they become more callous, not the sweet person they used to be. I have not done research in this area, but I've personally seen changes as a result of alcohol use.

• **Will alcohol hinder my life?**

Only you can answer this one. Where are you in your life? Are you satisfied with your progress? Could you be further along without the alcohol part of your story? I always meet people reflecting on where they could be if they had never picked up that first drink. They regret the moment they ever started with the substance, the places it has taken them and all the associations they have lost because of it, and they tell me how they wish they had never been exposed to it. One of the biggest things they regret is how it took them away from their family. I think this is the most significant loss—how they were not there and raising their child or children because of alcohol. I'm sure the memory is painful.

Alcohol consumes your life and causes you to be so engulfed in yourself. That's what addiction does. It is selfish. It keeps you focused on satisfying your need. It takes your memory. It takes your money and time from you. You spend so much time addicted to alcohol that you may make it through a workday because you know you have to survive, but it's all to get home and return to alcohol.

As for children, some grow all the way to adulthood with an absent mother or father who drank all those years. It's tough to accept and navigate through life knowing that your parents were consumed with alcohol.

Are you honest about what alcohol is doing in your life? I tell my patients that honesty is a sign of recovery. The more open you become, the more you demonstrate you are accomplishing your goal of sobriety.

- **Can I die if I continue to drink?**

Yes, you could. You can damage your liver by excessively drinking—you poison it with the toxic effects of alcohol. Then, the liver stops breaking down fat, causing it to be stored in the liver so you develop what's called a fatty liver, which irritates and damages the organ as well.[41] Cirrhosis is a scarred liver. It is a result of inflammation or swelling that heals as a scar, and that scar is hard, nonfunctioning liver tissue that inhibits the functioning of the liver overall.[42] Cirrhosis takes place after about ten years of heavy drinking, in 10% to 20% of people who drink this way.[43] I have provided care to several people with cirrhosis. They each had a large abdomen full of fluid because the liver became backed up and fluid drained to the place of least resistance, which is the abdomen. This condition is called ascites.[44] Their skin was yellow due to the liver's inability to break down old red blood cells, which turn yellow after 120 days. The liver breaks them down and rids them from the body, but when the liver is scarred in the case of cirrhosis, its functionality is

---

[41] WebMD (2021, November 4). Fatty Liver Disease (Hepatic Steatosis). https://www.webmd.com. Retrieved May 25, 2023, from https://www.webmd.com/hepatitis/fatty-liver-disease.

[42] University of Michigan Health (n.d.). Alcohol Related Liver Disease. https://www.uofmhealth.org. Retrieved May 25, 2023, from https://www.uofmhealth.org/conditions-treatments/digestive-and-liver-health/alcohol-related-liver-disease#:~:text=Alcohol%20Related%20Cirrhosis%3A%20The%20most,or%20more%20years%20of%20drinking.

[43] Ibid.

[44] Facty health (2019, December 4). 10 Facts About Ascites You Should Know. https://Facty.com. Retrieved May 25, 2023, from https://facty.com/conditions/digestion/10-facts-about-ascites-you-should-know/2/.

impaired. This condition is called jaundice.[45] As more functions of the liver cease, the person's complications increase, until ultimately there is total liver failure. We can't live without a liver, and so the person dies.

This is just one of the ways continuing to drink could cost you your life.

## Social Effects

• **What is my drinking doing to my social life?**

You feel like you are the hippest, most celebrated person in the club or social gathering. You make people laugh. But are you sure that they're laughing at what you are saying—or are they laughing at you? Could it be that people are not engaged in what you're talking about, because you are drinking so much that sometimes you don't even know what you're saying? And could they be mocking you? Could they be ashamed of you or embarrassed by your behavior? Does nothing reach you no matter what they say, and you never seem to get their warnings or admonishments to stop drinking? And then, after the party ends, can you get in your car and safely drive and not be at risk of harming yourself or others? Or do you have to be taken home because of the safety risk?

Take an honest look at what drinking is doing to your social life. Maybe ask the people who are around you, "Hey, how do you see me when I'm out and when I'm drinking?

---

[45] WebMD (2022, August 28). Jaundice: Why It Happens in Adults. https://www.webmd.com. Retrieved May 25, 2023, from https://www.webmd.com/hepatitis/jaundice-why-happens-adults.

What kind of person do you see me as? Do I make a fool of myself?"

It all seems like a typical social life. You're getting out. You're a part of the community. But ask yourself: Am I safe? Am I harmful? Am I an embarrassment? Am I funny for the wrong reasons? Or do I handle my drink responsibly and say a few things, but have it all under control? Do I ever do more than drink? When I loosen up a little bit, do I know how to turn it off and stop? Or should I choose not to be with this substance? Should I choose to separate myself from it?

Only you know whether this applies to you. What is your drinking doing to your social life?

• **Why am I more sociable when I drink?**

There's a short and sweet answer to this one: because your inhibitions decrease. There's something in your brain called GABA, which is an inhibitory neurotransmitter that alcohol has an effect on. It can lower your GABA by a significant amount. So, when you're drinking, you're just more likely to say and do things that you wouldn't normally say and do.[46]

You become more relaxed and maybe more talkative. You might become the life of the party. But alcohol can do a lot of different things to people. You might find that people cannot understand you when you drink, because you aren't who you were before you started drinking. And sometimes

---

[46] Georgetown Behavioral Health (1, January 1). GABA and Alcohol: How Drinking Leads to Anxiety. https://www.Gbhoh.com/Gaba-And-Alcohol-How-Drinking-Leads-To-Anxiety. Retrieved September 20, 2023, from https://www.gbhoh.com/gaba-and-alcohol-how-drinking-leads-to-anxiety/#:~:text=How%20does%20alcohol%20affect%20GABA,stress%2C%20depression%2C%20and%20paranoia.

people won't even want to be around you when you get started drinking because they know you're going to change—they know that something is going to get out of hand. Maybe they know that you may be arrested, or the whole night might be spoiled because once you start drinking, you're not going to be able to stop. You're probably going to black out. You're probably going to wet yourself. It is going to be a mess. And so, they may understand you for the first part of the evening when you're just a few drinks in, but once things get heavier, they're not going to understand who you are, and that won't be good.

• **How does alcohol influence my sex life?**

Some people find alcohol to be an aphrodisiac—it heightens them, it pumps them up and makes them want to get real kinky and freaky. Their inhibitions are down, and the changed chemicals in their brain have made them more open to trying stuff and doing things. That can be risky, because sometimes you may do those kinds of things and not protect yourself. Or you may do things with a person who doesn't have your best interests in mind, doesn't love you, or could be taking advantage of you because you are intoxicated.[47]

Or maybe you were at a point where you knew things were going bad and you told the person to stop and that person just wasn't trying to hear that. And now you're left with a scar, maybe even a pregnancy or a disease, because alcohol influenced your sex life. And that's just too bad. I

---

[47] National Institute on Alcohol Abuse and Alcoholism (2021, February 1). Make a Difference: Talk to Your Child About Alcohol – Parents. https://www.niaaa.nih.gov. Retrieved April 19, 2023, from https://www.niaaa.nih.gov/sites/default/files/publications/NIAAA_Make_a_Difference_English_1.pdf.

mean, that's just unfair. It shouldn't ever happen. And so, if this is speaking to you, maybe take an inventory and look at how alcohol affects your sex life.

I don't think anything that affects your sex life is good. I think you should be able to make a decision, you should be fully competent. You should be in total agreement with what you do sexually. You should not be persuaded or tricked or misguided in any way when it comes to sexuality. That's a very personal thing, and who you have sex with is very personal. And you should not need alcohol to get you in the mood, or to numb you because you are performing sexual acts that include monies. Alcohol should never have to be a part of your sex life, because it takes the genuineness away. It takes the sincerity away.

## Effects on Your Family

•   **What is my drinking doing to my family?**

Many of us have a family. We have parents, we have siblings, some may have children, and drinking impacts them all. I saw it as a child—I saw drinking in the family. It started OK, it started with fun and laughter and music playing, but sometimes it went pretty left or got out of control. Arguments broke out, fights, and just really scary stuff that no child should ever have been exposed to.

No child should ever have to see people change and become someone else right before their eyes, like Dr. Jekyll and Mr. Hyde. You say to yourself, "Who is this person? Who is this?" And you have to find a corner, a spot to be safe, because you can't leave home, you can't get out, you can't call for help—you're just a child. And then, after the party is over, you stand there and cry, plead, and ask for the behavior to stop. And in some families, the behavior stops, but in others, it never does. The people continue to drink and drink. And it either makes that child hate drinking or hate their family— or it might make them decide, "Well, I might as well join them. I might as well be just like them. I mean, they are my examples. If they do it, it must be OK."

So, two types of people can come out of this kind of experience: one who hates drinking and then another who decides, "This is the way to go." Drinking does so much to families, so much to the community, so much to society.

It's not just children who are affected. Someone whose spouse has an alcohol use disorder might not want to leave because they'll lose their home or their lifestyle. Often the spouse is able to get up and go to work, able to be productive, or they might be in a very tolerant job. And people can be very secretive; they often don't want to let others know what they're dealing with. So they tolerate the abuse—the mental abuse, the physical abuse—for years and years.

• **Will my family leave me if I continue to drink?**

They could—they very well could. They very well could get enough strength, enough courage, enough intolerance of you that they conclude that there's no way to manage this but to leave. And that would probably be good for their lives. Because if they have to look back over fifteen or twenty years they endured your alcohol use disorder and how it impacted their children, maybe even their grandchildren, that will be so unfair. And sometimes families do leave. But I encourage families to join support groups like Al-Anon so that they get to understand the disease of addiction. I hope they will not just throw up their hands and be done with you, divorce you, estrange you from the family, but try to be understanding and help you in your disease.

We use the word *disease* because it means abnormalities and dysfunction, which are taking place here as a result of alcohol.[48] The disease takes place as a result of the introduction of alcohol and the continued use of it, causing things to be out of order. So, we call it an alcohol use disorder. And sometimes, with this alcohol use disorder, families do not have the patience to stay; they do not have the ability to continue to suffer, because it is suffering. It is like being in a house with a monster, being in a house with someone unpredictable, someone you're not sure what they might do.

They might laugh; they might be happy. But they may become incredibly paranoid. They may become violent. They may break things or hurt people who have done nothing to them at all. They may go to jail; they may drive a car and put everybody in the car and on the highway with them at risk of being killed. And so, will your family leave? They could. There are families who have left, husbands who have left, wives who have left and children who have got out of the home, because they saw so much and nothing seemed to change. So, they made the change themselves.

I encourage you to make a change, before others around you who love you make a change. And I encourage family members not to throw in the towel, but to join support groups like Al-Anon. These groups help families and loved ones to understand the person who is suffering from the disease, not to get angry and mad, and to just say, "Well, they

---

[48] National Institute on Alcohol Abuse and Alcoholism (2023, April 1). Alcohol's Effects on Health Research-based information on drinking and its impact. https://www.niaaa.nih.gov/. Retrieved May 19, 2023, from https://www.niaaa.nih.gov/publications/brochures-and-fact-sheets/understanding-alcohol-use-disorder.

could change; they just want to be this way." This person is enthralled with the disease of addiction that has overtaken them and has left them powerless. And you are the voice of reality. You are on the other side, helping them manage, helping them to see that there's a better way, that there's another side to the story. You could be the bridge that brings them over to help and security.

If you're asking whether your family might leave you, I hope they won't. But I also hope that they will become a support to you by being educated and informed.

- **Will my children be influenced by my drinking and turn into drinkers?**

You could influence them. They see parents as authority figures. They see parents as examples and think, "If they do it, then I should do it also." They could follow in your path. Alternatively, they could be turned off by your drinking and begin to dislike you, hate alcohol or hate anyone who drinks alcohol.

The NIAAA says, "Research shows that children of actively involved parents are less likely to drink alcohol. However, if parents provide alcohol to their kids (even small amounts), have positive attitudes about drinking and engage in alcohol misuse, adolescents have an increased risk of misusing alcohol."[49]

---

49 National Institute on Alcohol Abuse and Alcoholism (2023, March 1). Alcohol's Effects on Health Research-based information on drinking and its impact. https://www.niaaa.nih.gov. Retrieved May 27, 2023, from https://www.niaaa.nih.gov/publications/brochures-and-fact-sheets/underage-drinking.

- **Will my children hate me if I don't stop drinking?**

Yes, they could. They could be very resentful of how you were not there, how your time was spent in drinking and having a good time, having a social life. And they could hate how addiction took over your life and robbed them of a parent.

I once talked with a young lady who was an only child and her father was a drinker, and all her life, he drank and he just was not there. When she got older, she tried to form a bond with him, but he continued to drink. And she had to set lots of limits with him to let him know that she wasn't going to be tolerant of his behavior. So, it was a relationship loss. And she was his only child—he only had her to love— but instead, he loved alcohol more than his own flesh and blood. I think that's a pretty tough and upsetting experience for an only child to have, where a parent forsakes the love of their child because of a drink, because of alcohol, and robs that child of the love that they so much deserved.

So, let's try not to do that. Let's try not to make alcohol so important that children are forgotten, are forsaken, because you are so deep in your addiction to alcohol. I do hope you turn around. I do hope you see that a life you helped create is much more important than all those bottles.

- **Why do my children fear me because of my drinking?**

Children can become afraid of their authority figures, their parents or those who are their guardians, if they have an alcohol use disorder because alcohol changes who you are. As you drink, you change. And it can make children very fearful and concerned about who is now in their life.

You may also make bad decisions with that child because you've allowed alcohol to impair your mind. People start out having alcohol under control. But eventually, over time, alcohol controls them. You start out only drinking on the weekends. But after a while, the more and more you consume, the more and more you become impaired and out of control, until alcohol is now dictating your life. And that could certainly make children very afraid and make them feel unsafe.

You have become unpredictable. After all, alcohol causes you to have mood changes and to say and do things that you wouldn't do when sober, which would make anybody untrusting. I'm a witness to this after being audiotaped in my blackout.

So this is one more good reason to want to stop drinking: It will definitely impact the people who love you, including your children. And when trust is broken, it isn't easy to reestablish. Not drinking, being in recovery, will not necessarily make your children feel safe around you right away. It will take some time for them to watch your life and watch you change for the better before they may start to trust you again.

- **Why don't my children want anything to do with me because of my drinking history?**

Some of my patients have children who don't want anything to do with them. They've fallen out of their relationship with their parents. Many of those parents were under the influence a lot of the time, said hurtful things, weren't responsible, didn't pay the bills, and caused their living situation to deteriorate. And maybe their kids felt like they didn't even really have a mother or a father because they were so wrapped up in drinking. That's a lot of pain that will take some time to heal.

You can't expect that because you went into a program, everybody will come and embrace you and say: "OK, I'm putting all the things that I went through with you behind me."

It's going to take some time. It's going to take some therapy. It's going to take a process before they want anything to do with you. They may eventually be able to trust you; they may be able to feel like you can have a part in their life.

Depending on how much you drank, when you started drinking or how much experience they have, they may only know you as a drinker. They may not even know you as a sober parent. So, be considerate, do not be so hard, and try to understand why your children may be the way they are toward you. You need to take some responsibility for that.

The longer you indulged in alcohol, the more likely problems were to develop. Many people say, "Well. My life was manageable. I went to work." But I don't think that gives a complete picture. You probably had enough sense not to want to be put out of your home. You didn't want to be homeless. That doesn't mean you were functioning well as a parent.

All those years of damage have their effect. So, be patient; be understanding that it's going to take time, maybe a lot of time. And you can't dictate the time. You can't dictate when people should forgive you, trust you now and welcome you back. It's going to be their call. It's their life.

- **Do I need to stop drinking in front of my family?**

Yes. Parents should never show their kids their drinking. It's a poor example. I have many stories from patients whose mothers or fathers drank alcohol and how that model contributed to their drinking.

One of the worst stories I've heard is of a twenty-four-year-old man who started consuming alcohol when he was eight years old. He had a grandfather who thought it was cute to place a small glass of alcohol at the end of the table just in reach for his grandson to take a sip. It may have been appealing to him. He must have had a severe alcohol use disorder to do something like that. He was out of his mind to do such an awful act. The downside to all of this is that the kid developed a taste for alcohol and continued to drink well into his twenties, until he was diagnosed with severe cirrhosis of the liver. To be a candidate for a liver transplant, he had to enter treatment for his alcohol use disorder, to show that he was serious about not drinking. His grandfather had planted the seed. That child was now an adult suffering from a disease of alcohol use that had destroyed his liver. I felt pity for this young man. It was not his fault. He didn't have a choice in the matter. What a shame.

There is data to support not drinking in front of your children; according to the NIAAA, a child brought up in a home with an alcoholic parent has a 25% chance of becoming a person with an alcohol use disorder. Pretty alarming.

• **My parents introduced me to alcohol. Why did they do that?**

I think parents who drink just don't know better. I don't think that they're working to the best of their judgment. I think the worst example a parent can give is to let their children see them drink. It would have been better if they'd hid it. You would be angry if they hid it and lied to you too, but just to openly sit out and drink so you watched them get wasted and saw their behavior? That wasn't a good example. And I'm sure it left a pretty bad taste in your mouth.

When my patients tell me stories that their parents drank—their mother drank, or their father drank, or their father died from cirrhosis—they are saddened about their deaths, but they seem like they're saddened that they were robbed. They were robbed of a parent who died way before their time, and they never really got a chance to enjoy them. They see alcohol as something that took over their parent and caused their early death. They always talk about alcohol in a regretful way.

Some parents may be doing what was done to them. Maybe they were introduced to alcohol by their parents and are following that pattern. Maybe they think it is innocent and won't cause harm because it's just a swig or a small amount and it's amusing to see the effects on the child.

Whatever way you look at it, it is not good and it should've never happened.

We can't change the past. But we can work toward forgiveness and change the future, and that might mean not holding resentment toward your parents if you had this experience. It may even require counseling to move beyond that obstacle in your past. But I believe that if you never find a way to forgive them, it will keep you bound.

• **Can my family get help for living with me, a drinker?**

Yes, your family can get help. There's a great group called Al-Anon.[50] Your family can find a local chapter and get

---

[50] Al-Anon (n.d.). Al-Anon Meetings. https://Al-Anon.org. Retrieved June 22, 2023, from https://al-anon.org/al-anon-meetings/?gclid=CjwKCAjw1M ajBhAcEiwAagW9MWLbKkeT_xy3LzqqlrCPGizhwuMll42PabUhsVa-PRtEJiFEjlcGjRoCiH0QAvD_BwE.

some support and some help with understanding how to live with you. They can learn how to manage with a person who is a drinker and what they can do when your drinking spills over to the lives of your children and to the people who love you. Nowadays, all these groups and supports are available online too.

And your family may need help, too, because they're furious. Sometimes they can be very embarrassed about your behavior. They may have to take care of you if your health is starting to suffer. They may even have to help financially support the household because of the toll drinking has taken on your life. And then there are the legal ramifications of your drinking. So, family members can definitely benefit from a support group like Al-Anon.

If you are a family member of someone with an alcohol use disorder, you can also seek out therapists who provide substance abuse treatment, learn some coping skills and learn how to manage with your family member. Reach out and get some help. Don't try to do it on your own. It is complicated, and you will need support and service.

# CHAPTER 8

## The Dangers of Alcohol Use Disorder

If there wasn't something dangerous about alcohol, this book wouldn't have been written. It would be a waste of your time and mine. Interestingly, I came across a scripture about the dangers of alcohol, Proverbs 23:30–35:

> Those who linger long at the wine,
> Those who go in search of mixed wine.
>
> Do not look on the wine when it is red,
> When it sparkles in the cup,
> When it swirls around smoothly;
>
> At the last it bites like a serpent,
> And stings like a viper.
>
> Your eyes will see strange things,
> And your heart will utter perverse things.

Yes, you will be like one who lies down in the midst of the sea,
Or like one who lies at the top of the mast, saying:

"They have struck me, but I was not hurt;
They have beaten me, but I did not feel it.
When shall I awake, that I may seek another drink?"

- **What is alcohol tolerance?**

Alcohol tolerance is the brain adjusting to alcohol, trying to compensate for what you're putting into your body and trying to keep you at what we call homeostasis or balance. This means that when you drink a certain amount, the body will balance its chemicals to reduce the effect of that amount.[51] You will have to drink even more to get an impact. Tolerance is something the brain has taken upon itself to normalize you. And as a result of that normalization, you're not satisfied with the effects of drinking, so you need to drink more to alter the brain to feel the high and the pleasure from alcohol.

- **What is a blackout, and what is passing out?**

A blackout happens when a person drinks an excessive amount of alcohol over a short period. It causes memory not to be retained. It affects the brain's hippocampus, so the per-

---

[51] Washburn House A Promises Behavioral Health Company (2022, January 25). The Truth About Alcohol Tolerance. https://www.washburnhouse.com/addiction-recovery-blog. Retrieved September 21, 2023, from https://www.washburnhouse.com/addiction-recovery-blog/the-truth-about-alcohol-tolerance-2/.

son is unable to store new memory. They're intoxicated very quickly. They reach a blood alcohol level of 0.08, which is the legal limit of intoxication. The person gets to this level in about two hours.[52]

They are conscious, and they are saying and doing things, but they're unable to remember later what they've said and done. They may fight, they may curse. They may act out. I know for myself as a teenager, having blacked out, I wouldn't have had any recall of what happened if I didn't have it recorded. And because it was recorded, I got to hear myself. I could listen to my slurred speech. I could hear my inappropriate comments. And that was only because I listened to the recording.

It's a terrifying thing, a blackout. It is very frightening that you could say and do something without recall—your brain just won't remember it. I've heard stories of people who blacked out, drove hundreds of miles to other states and didn't even know how they got there. Very dangerous, very frightening. Having been there, I could testify about that, with absolute confidence of how that works and what happened.

The difference between that and passing out is that when you pass out, you drink alcohol, become unconscious and cold, fall asleep and don't engage in any activities. Passing out is being in a sleep state where your motor activities are not stimulated. You're just put to sleep, unlike in a blackout,

52 National Institute on Alcohol Abuse and Alcoholism (2023, February 1). Alcohol's Effects on Health. https://www.niaaa.nih.gov. Retrieved September 21, 2023, from https://www.niaaa.nih.gov/publications/brochures-and-fact-sheets/interrupted-memories-alcohol-induced-blackouts#:~:text=Alcohol%2Drelated%20blackouts%20are%20gaps,brain%20area%20called%20the%20hippocampus.

when you're conscious but unable to retain new memories of what you're saying and doing.[53]

- **What are alcohol withdrawals like?**

That's a good question and deserves a good answer. The American Society of Addiction Medicine states:

> *In those with physiologic dependence on alcohol, the clinical manifestation of alcohol withdrawal begins 6 to 24 hours after the last drink (or after marked reduction in the quantity of alcohol consumed), sometimes arising before the blood alcohol level has returned to zero.*[54]

When a person quits or reduces alcohol, the depressant effects of alcohol or the slowing down of brain activity begins to try to normalize. The body is trying to get back to the way it used to be, and in the course of the brain trying to balance itself out, it gets overly stimulated; the nervous system revs up.[55] It may start with the feeling of anxiety, as though they anticipate some impending danger. This anxiety can be mild, moderate or severe.

If withdrawals persist, the person may experience hallucinations.

---

[53] Ibid.
[54] Ries, R. K., Fiellin, D. A., Miller, S. C., & Saitz, R. (2014). *The ASAM principles of addiction medicine*. Wolters Kluwer.
[55] Ibid.

*Visual hallucinations are most common and frequently involve some type of animal life, such as seeing a dog or rodent in the room.*[56]

If the person has not sought medical care at this point, the progression of withdrawals can lead to seizures.

*Withdrawal seizures usually begin within 8 to 24 hours after the person's last drink and may occur before the blood alcohol level has returned to zero.*

*In addition, the risk of withdrawal seizure appears to be in part genetically determined and is increased in patients with past withdrawal seizures or in those who are undergoing concurrent withdrawals from benzodiazepines or other sedative–hypnotic drugs.*[57]

The last and most serious of alcohol withdrawal is DTs or delirium tremens. Fortunately, DTs is very uncommon due to the advancements in care and treatment of alcohol use disorder.[58] I have heard people describe this as seeing pink elephants. I'm not sure if that still occurs, but certainly a person with delirium tremens experiences great confusion.

When I was working at a treatment center in West Baltimore, we had a person who was going through alcohol withdrawals. We were treating him with a short-acting medication called Ativan or lorazepam, which is a benzodiazepine. (Other common ones are Valium, Librium and Serax.) These medicines mimic alcohol in the brain, and they help the ner-

---

[56] Ibid.
[57] Ibid.
[58] Ibid.

vous system to stabilize.[59] It's as if the person is receiving alcohol, but in a less toxic form. This person was receiving Ativan probably every two hours, but he was increasingly becoming confused and his blood pressure was getting higher and higher. He had classic symptoms of delirium tremens: confusion, hyperstimulation of the nervous system, blood pressure increases and a fast pulse rate. The person became more than what the residential facility could handle. He was running throughout the building and needed medical attention. Our medical director agreed that he needed another level of care, and emergency medical services (EMS) was called. EMS put him in a restraint and onto a stretcher. He entered a nearby hospital and was in their intensive care unit for about a week. Delirium tremens is a medical emergency.

- **Are the tremors I'm experiencing a result of me not having a drink?**

Look at your hands when you stop drinking. Do you develop tremors?

Some people will have tremors from withdrawing from alcohol. We'll see it in the hands and even in the tongue—you can stick your tongue out and look in the mirror and see tremors. This is your brain trying to balance out, now that it's free of alcohol. Alcohol is a depressant, which means it slows down brain activity. When you stop drinking or reduce your drinking, your excitatory system tries to regulate or modulate your brain chemistry to get back into balance.[60]

---

[59] Ibid.

[60] WebMD (2021, November 26). What Is Alcohol Withdrawal? https://www.webmd.com. Retrieved August 10, 2023, from https://www.webmd.com/mental-health/addiction/alcohol-withdrawal-symptoms-treatments.

So you may see tremors when you stop drinking; you might even have a seizure. And worse, you might go into delirium tremens, a very severe case of alcohol withdrawal usually two to three days after you have stopped drinking, if you didn't taper down or enter into a detox where they could give you a benzodiazepine or antianxiety medication to get you off alcohol safely.

We've already talked about DTs, and what is happening there is total brain stimulation. A very low percentage of people, somewhere around 5%, will experience that. And a very small percentage of those people may die from it.[61] But the world of medicine today is good at treating alcohol withdrawal, so that doesn't occur too often.

- **What is a wet brain?**

This is a term related to a serious brain condition called Wernicke–Korsakoff syndrome (WK syndrome), associated with chronic alcohol misuse.[62] In WK syndrome, two different brain conditions, Wernicke disease and Korsakoff psy-

61  National Library of Medicine (2023, August 14). Delirium Tremens. https://www.ncbi.nlm.nih.gov. Retrieved August 21, 2023, from https://www.ncbi.nlm.nih.gov/books/NBK482134/#:~:text=The%20 lifetime%20risk%20for%20developing,prior%20history%20of%20 seizures.

62  Dictionary and Thesaraus.com (n.d.). Wernicke-Korsakoff syndrome. https://www.dictionary.com. Retrieved September 19, 2023, from https://www.dictionary.com/browse/wernicke-korsakoff-syndrome; National Institute of Neurological Disorders or Strokes (2023, January 30). Wernicke-Korsakoff Syndrome. https://www.ninds. nih.gov. Retrieved September 19, 2023, from https://www. ninds.nih.gov/health-information/disorders/wernicke-korsakoff-syndrome#:~:text=What%20is%20Wernicke%2DKorsakoff%20 syndrome,(Wernicke%2DKorsakoff%20syndrome).

chosis, happen together. They result from brain damage associated with chronic drinking, which is drinking most days of the week, eight or more standard drinks for women and fifteen or more standard drinks for men, for a period of six months or longer. People with WK syndrome have a vitamin B1 deficiency. People with severe alcohol use disorder have less ability to absorb thiamine from foods like fortified breakfast cereals, fish and beans. A person with the disease might experience problems with vision, movement, language, sleep, memory and motivation due to the areas of the brain that are affected. They can also experience confusion, lack of energy, feeling really cold and lack of muscle coordination that can affect their posture and balance and can lead to tremors. Vision problems include abnormal eye movement and double vision.[63]

The good news is that Wernicke disease is reversible with prompt treatment of the symptoms. Without treatment, it may respond more slowly or may not be completely reversible. Wernecke disease can progress to Korsakoff psychosis, which is not reversible.[64]

The symptoms of Korsakoff psychosis include potentially severe memory impairment and problems forming new memories, making up inaccurate stories about events (called confabulations) and hallucinations (seeing or hearing things that are not really there).[65]

---

[63] National Institute of Neurological Disorders or Strokes (2023, January 30). Wernicke-Korsakoff Syndrome. https://www.ninds.nih.gov. Retrieved September 19, 2023, from https://www.ninds.nih.gov/health-information/disorders/wernicke-korsakoff-syndrome#:~:text=What%20is%20Wernicke%2DKorsakoff%20syndrome,(Wernicke%2DKorsakoff%20syndrome).
[64] Ibid.
[65] Ibid.

I worked with someone years ago who had a family member with this serious brain condition. They had a long history of drinking alcohol, and the symptoms were not reversible. This person required total care in a nursing home facility. They were confused and could not feed or wash themselves. I was sad to hear this report. Up to that point, I had only read about WK syndrome, sometimes called wet brain, which is an old and stigmatizing term taken from American addiction centers stemming from an inaccurate belief that individuals willfully contracted WK syndrome due to prolonged alcohol misuse.

A person is diagnosed by getting a good history of their alcohol consumption and their symptoms. Doctors may be able to confirm the diagnosis with a magnetic resonance imaging scan (an MRI). It is worth noting that WK syndrome may result from other conditions that involve malnutrition and vitamin B1 deficiency, such as cancers that cause excessive vomiting, anorexia, gastrointestinal problems and bariatric surgery, but those causes are far less common than those associated with severe alcohol use disorder.[66]

• **What happens if I have liver damage?**

A cirrhotic liver brings about a lot of problems. The liver stores blood. It acts as a reservoir and holds up to one pint of blood, or 13% of all the blood in the body.[67] But when the liver is damaged, it is not able to store blood properly.

---

[66] Ibid.

[67] Johns Hopkins Medicine (n.d.). Liver: Anatomy and Functions. https://www.hopkinsmedicine.org/. Retrieved September 19, 2023, from https://www.hopkinsmedicine.org/health/conditions-and-diseases/liver-anatomy-and-functions#:~:text=The%20liver%20holds%20about%20one,supply%20at%20any%20given%20moment.

That causes a fluid backup, and a condition called ascites can develop. With ascites, fluid collects in spaces in your abdomen.[68] I have seen this with people. They have an enormous abdomen that is filled with fluid. The fluid is plasma, which is the liquid part of our blood, what some may call the water part of the blood. It accumulates in the abdomen, the part of the body that provides the least resistance. Our arms and legs are constantly moving and leave no room for large deposits of fluid buildup, though you can get some fluid buildup in the lower legs. In ascites, lots of fluid can accumulate. This causes shortness of breath, particularly when the person lies flat, which pushes the fluid against the wall separating the lungs and the abdomen. Periodically the person will have to have it drained off.

Secondly, cirrhosis causes jaundice, which makes the person's skin turn yellow. The sclera, the white part of the eyes, turns yellow too. The liver does an amazing job of getting rid of old red blood cells after 120 days, the length of time our red blood cells keep their color; after that time, they lose their pigmentation and become yellow. "Bilirubin is formed when hemoglobin (the part of red blood cells that carries oxygen) is broken down as part of the normal process of recycling old or damaged red blood cells."[69] When a per-

---

[68] Johns Hopkins Medicine (n.d.). Ascites. https://www.hopkinsmedicine.org/. Retrieved September 19, 2023, from https://www.hopkinsmedicine.org/health/conditions-and-diseases/ascites.

[69] Merck Manual Consumer Version (2023, January 31). Jaundice in Adults. https://www.merckmanuals.com. Retrieved September 20, 2023, from https://www.merckmanuals.com/home/liver-and-gallbladder-disorders/manifestations-of-liver-disease/jaundice-in-adults#:~:text=Jaundice%20occurs%20when%20there%20is,blood%E2%80%94a%20condition%20called%20hyperbilirubinemia.&text=Bilirubin%20is%20formed%20when%20hemoglobin,or%20damaged%20red%20blood%20cells.

son's liver is damaged, it can't filter out the bilirubin, and the person gets jaundice.

Thirdly, when the liver is malfunctioning due to inflammation from alcohol, the job of excreting ammonia from the breakdown of muscle becomes a problem. Ammonia is a waste product made by your body during the digestion of protein. If your liver is not able to break down ammonia, it can accumulate in the blood and cause damage. High ammonia levels can lead to serious health problems, including brain damage and even death, according to MEDLINEplus.[70]

I have treated people with high ammonia levels due to liver damage. Some of them have had to take a medicine called lactulose or Enulose.[71] It helps to remove excess ammonia through defecation. Some people hate going to the bathroom frequently and therefore stop taking their lactulose as prescribed, and they then become confused and require a hospital stay. They find it challenging to decide between going to the bathroom frequently or becoming confused and sedated, maybe ending up in a coma or even dying. I hope you or your loved one choose to avoid hospitalization.

---

[70] MedlinePlus (2023, September 19). Ammonia Levels. Retrieved September 20, 2023, from https://medlineplus.gov/lab-tests/ammonia-levels.

[71] National Library of Medicine (2022, July 11). Lactulose. https://www.ncbi.nlm.nih.gov/. Retrieved September 20, 2023, from https://www.ncbi.nlm.nih.gov/books/NBK536930/#:~:text=Lactulose%20is%20used%20in%20preventing,management%20of%20subacute%20clinical%20encephalopathy.

- **Does drinking alcohol cause hepatitis?**

Drinking alcohol can cause hepatitis. *Hepa-* means liver and *-itis* means inflamed or swollen. The most common causes are alcohol and hepatitis C, which is a virus.[72]

The liver can become damaged in two ways. When a person drinks, the liver thinks alcohol is the most important thing to break down and will bypass breaking down fat from foods, so fat is stored in the liver. People may then develop a fatty liver, which causes inflammation.[73]

The second way that alcohol can damage the liver is directly. When you drink more alcohol than the liver can break down—which is one twelve-ounce beer, one five-ounce glass of wine or one to one and a half ounces of gin or vodka for a woman in an hour, and twice that amount in an hour for a man, due to a man's body having more water and more muscle—the excess alcohol causes a toxicity to the very organ that's responsible for breaking down alcohol.[74]

We can see this damage to the liver and the enzymes it produces. If you drink, go to your doctor and have them check your liver, or have a test done to look at liver function.[75] The good news is that many liver function tests return to normal after a few weeks once alcohol is no longer being consumed. Of course, this might not apply if you have reached the final stages of liver damage, such as needing a new liver or being in stage four liver disease, the worst stage. Hopefully,

---

[72] Ibid.

[73] Ibid.

[74] Ibid.

[75] Cleveland Clinic (2022, November 9). Liver Function Tests. Retrieved September 20, 2023, from https://my.clevelandclinic.org/health/diagnostics/17662-liver-function-tests.

that's not your story and any damage can be reversed for you or your loved one.

• **What is pancreatitis?**

I occasionally have met patients experiencing pancreatitis from drinking alcohol. The most common complaints are abdominal and back pain. People may have to be hospitalized for several days to allow their pancreas to heal.

The pancreas is a banana-shaped organ behind the stomach. It releases insulin and glucagon to help provide energy for our bodies, and it also releases three powerful digestive enzymes, the chemicals that help the body digest starches, fats, and proteins. What happens to the pancreas when you drink is alcohol is toxic. The pancreas becomes swollen, stopping the release of the enzymes, which then begin to digest the pancreas itself. As a result of this blockage, the person experiences a considerable amount of pain in the abdomen that radiates to the back. The course of treatment is to provide IV fluids and keep the person from eating anything, because that will only stimulate the pancreas to release more enzymes, and more enzymes will increase the pain. Pancreatitis resolves in about three to seven days, and the person can return to life with one word of caution, and you already know what that is. Don't drink alcohol.

The most common reasons for pancreatitis are a blocked gallbladder and alcohol consumption.

• **What does alcohol do to the developing brain?**

Alcohol does a lot to the developing brain. And we in the medical field really try to tell young people not to drink because the brain is maturing, and alcohol does interfere with that maturation process. That's why you're told not to drink before you're twenty-one—even though the brain is still developing, for men up to about twenty-four or twenty-five, and for women about twenty-three, as their brains mature a little faster than men's. But alcohol slows down the development of the brain. It causes it not to mature as quickly as it would if you were not drinking alcohol.[76]

- **What does alcohol do to women that it doesn't do to men?**

Interestingly, women are created differently. Their bodies are not made with a particular enzyme in their stomach that helps to break down alcohol as effectively as men can, so women experience a much more significant effect from drinking than men. Women also have less water and muscle in their bodies than men. All this means that alcohol acts differently in a woman's body than in a man's.[77]

---

[76] National Institute on Alcohol Abuse and Alcoholism (2023, September 1). Alcohol's Effects on Health Research-based information on drinking and its impact. https://www.niaaa.nih.gov. Retrieved September 20, 2023, from https://www.niaaa.nih.gov/publications/alcohol-and-adolescent-brain#:~:text=More%20and%20more%20research%20suggests,time%E2%80%94perhaps%20even%20into%20adulthood.

[77] Harvard Health Publishing (2013, January 13). Ask the doctor: Why does alcohol affect women differently? https://www.Health.Harvard.edu. Retrieved September 20, 2023, from https://www.health.harvard.edu/womens-health/why-does-alcohol-affect-women-differently#:~:text=Also%2C%20women%20have%20less%20alcohol,account%20differences%20in%20body%20weight.

# CHAPTER 9

# I Heard There's a Way Out from Alcohol

The old saying is, "If there's a will, there's a way." I hope you agree. There is a way out of alcohol too. You first have to have a willing desire to change from drinking to being sober. I don't believe in cutting down—that's a game people play with their lives. Don't be in that group.

If you are drinking to a level that has any impact on the control you have over your life, in my opinion, you can't simply become a lighter drinker. You will always be at risk of wanting more, due to having a tolerance to alcohol. You must totally abstain. You might not agree, but that's my stance.

• **How does detox work?**

When you come into detox, there is an assessment of your drinking history and the possibility of withdrawals if you've ever had them, and they will check your vital signs. They will ask you some questions about how you are feeling. They'll look at your hands and at your tongue to see if there are any tremors, and you'll be medicated based on the type of symptoms, the things you say you're experiencing and what that medical professional is observing in you. Be honest about your history of alcohol use to the best of your ability. You'll be there for several days or weeks, depending on how severe an alcohol use disorder you have.

Sometimes trying to quit alcohol on your own can result in a bad outcome and a trip to the hospital via the emergency room. Detox is meant to safely help your body remove the poison of alcohol and to offer you medications like Librium, Valium, Ativan or Serax. These are medicines called benzodiazepines or antianxiety medications.[78] They mimic alcohol in the brain and they help to balance the hyperactivity that is happening there and in your nervous system, allowing you to get to a stable state and to return to what we call homeostasis, or balance. They bring you back to where you were before you had alcohol in your system. Like all medicines, they come with some side effects; the most common are drowsiness, lightheadedness, some confusion and nausea. The nurses and doctors are highly trained to manage these side effects and adjust the medicine as needed.

- **Is treatment for alcoholism a way to stop drinking?**

Absolutely. Treatment is a way for alcohol users to stop drinking. It helps them safely stop, keeps them monitored and helps them get the support they need in their families. Treatment works. Outpatient treatment is available virtually,

---

[78] GoodRX Health (2023, April 6). Which Medications Treat Alcohol Withdrawal Syndrome? How Benzos and Others Can Help. https://www.Goodrx.com. Retrieved September 20, 2023, from https://www.goodrx.com/conditions/alcohol-use-disorder/alcohol-withdrawal-medication.

and there are inpatient treatment options too. It depends on your needs. It depends on how long you have been drinking and what signs and symptoms you're experiencing from withdrawals. But treatment is readily available. It's just not utilized as much as it needs to be.

Not enough people utilize the medicines to help with this disorder. Let's talk about the medicines available for an AUD.

I see a good response to the medication naltrexone. Several of my patients have reported not desiring to drink alcohol. This is a 50 mg pill that's taken daily under observation by a nurse, after the patient takes a breathalyzer. The breathalyzer helps the person to be accountable. If you are at home, you can get a breathalyzer to help your loved one be accountable. Watching them take the medicine helps with accountability as well.

You won't get sick if you drink on Naltrexone. It's not like disulfiram (dye-sul-fe-ram) or Antabuse, which will make you sick if you consume alcohol while taking them. The biggest side effect associated with this medicine is nausea. Some people have complained that the nausea is hard to tolerate, so we recommend taking it with food in the stomach, or taking it at a lower dose of 25 mg and then slowly increasing the dose to 50 mg. One more side effect that I have heard complaints about is feeling tired or sluggish. In that case, the person can simply take it at night. Also, this medicine is very safe for the liver. Overall, this is the most prescribed medicine for the treatment of an alcohol use disorder. Naltrexone blocks the euphoric effects and feelings of intoxication and allows people with alcohol use disorders to reduce alcohol use and stay motivated to take the medication, stay in treatment and avoid relapses.[79]

Disulfiram or Antabuse is a medication used for someone serious about quitting alcohol. Sometimes a person will have an opioid use disorder and an alcohol use disorder together, and this medicine can help them not drink alcohol. If the person has tried a lot of treatments and they still drink, disulfiram or Antabuse is considered a deterrent.[80] It works by reducing the activity of the liver breaking down alcohol, and if you drink while taking it, you will experience vomiting, hot flashes, headache and general body discomfort. It can also cause some drowsiness. A patient's liver needs monitoring while the person is taking this medicine, as it can cause liver abnormalities. So routine liver testing is a must. In my experience, I have never seen the medicine discontinued because it was damaging the liver. I've seen some marvelous results with this for people who have had a difficult time quitting alcohol. The medicine gives them a real fear of how they will feel if they drink, and that may sound extreme, but so are the dangerous consequences of drinking alcohol.

Again, if you are living with a loved one taking disulfiram or Antabuse, you would want to monitor them at home taking their medicine, and if it's possible to invest in a breathalyzer, I say go for it. That's what we do in the treat-

---

[79] Substance Abuse and Mental Health Services Administration (2023, March 22). Medications, Counseling, and Related Conditions Main page content Medications for Substance Use Disorders. https://www.Samhsa. gov/Medications-Substance-Use-Disorders/Medications-Counseling-Related-Conditions. Retrieved September 20, 2023, from https:// www.samhsa.gov/medications-substance-use-disorders/medications-counseling-related-conditions#:~:text=Acamprosate%2C%20 disulfiram%2C%20and%20naltrexone%20are,participate%20in%20 a%20MAUD%20program.

[80] Ibid.

ment world. Perform a breathalyzer and watch the person take their dose, and on frequent occasion do a mouth check. People have been known to hold the medicine in hidden compartments of the mouth and later throw it away, so they can return to a life of drinking alcohol.

If the person is continuing to drink on the routine 250 mg dose and not experiencing the "godawful reaction" when alcohol meets disulfiram or Antabuse, then it's time to increase the dose, so you can get the benefit of the medicine.

Acamprosate or Campral is the least prescribed of all the alcohol treatments among the people I have provided care for. It is given three times a day and works by decreasing cravings. A person has to be able to comply with the routine of taking it three times a day. The most common side effect is diarrhea, and it is very safe to use, even for people with slight liver damage.[81]

- **Is it safe to enter detox? Will I experience withdrawals if I quit?**

Detox units are safe places. They're highly qualified to provide care. Over the decades, we've learned a lot about how to treat someone coming off alcohol. We know how to assess them, we know how to give them a score of how severe their AUD is, and we know how to move to another level of care if they need to go to the ICU. We've just learned so much about alcohol withdrawals that we understand how to safely detox people and keep them from dying. No matter how severe a person's disorder, we can help them stop drinking.

And so, I will vouch for the safety of detox programs. We're very qualified in the medical field to treat people coming off alcohol.

---

[81] Ibid.

# CHAPTER 10

## What Happens If I Stop Drinking?

When you stop drinking, you get a new life. It might be a life you haven't had before, because of years of drinking or starting to drink at a young age. You begin to get out of the fog of impairment and clearly see your future. But that doesn't mean it's easy to get there, and you might have some worries about what will happen if you get sober.

- **Why do I find the thought of quitting alcohol horrifying and painful?**

Well, because it is. What are you going to do with your life now? If you started drinking when you were a teenager, or you've been drinking since you can remember, it's what you know. It's what you've done, it's been a part of you, you're accustomed to it. It's a part of your routine, like putting your clothes on, brushing your teeth and going to work. It's been a very constant thing, and to quit now can be horrifying and can fill you with uncertainty.

But you have to weigh the benefits against the risks. Is it more beneficial for you to continue drinking or is it riskier? If

you add it up and you find that the risk outweighs the benefits, then you have to make a decision. You always have to be
evaluating whether it benefits you more to drink or to stop.
When the benefits of drinking are not as great as the risks of
drinking, then you need to stop. If the possible accidents,
blackouts, alcohol poisoning, disruptive behavior, inappropriate relationships, if all those things outweigh the joy, the
euphoria, the dopamine getting released in your brain, the
relaxation, you are going to have to find another way to relax
and enjoy life without putting yourself or other people at
such risk.

You may need medical intervention when it comes
to stopping alcohol because it's such a toxic substance that
abruptly stopping or even reducing your consumption of it
can cause you to have withdrawals, and those withdrawals can
be so severe that they can lead to death.[82] So is the thought
of quitting alcohol horrifying and painful? Absolutely it can
be. But wait—I have some good news. Detox is available,
and you can come into a hospital and safely get off alcohol.
It doesn't have to be horrifying, it doesn't have to be painful.
Just don't try to do it on your own.

- **What if I believe alcohol is everything to me?**

Sometimes people really do make alcohol their everything. It is what they get up with. It's what they go through
their day with. It is what is in their thoughts. They have an
obsession, meaning they're thinking about it; they have a
compulsion, meaning they're trying to get it. It consumes

---

[82] National Library of Medicine (1998, January 1). Complications
of Alcohol Withdrawal. https://www.ncbi.nlm.nih.gov. Retrieved
August 10, 2023, from https://www.ncbi.nlm.nih.gov/pmc/articles/
PMC6761825/.

their lives. And that's what addiction will do. Addiction to alcohol will consume your life. It will make your life center around it. At one time you had control. At one time you said no. At one time you put it aside. But now it says, "Let's go. Let's get a drink." It says, "No, I want you to take two." It says, "Don't pay that bill. Buy a drink instead." It tells you to maybe talk with this person or sleep with that person. It now dictates your whole life.

It becomes your everything, and you really don't have a lot of choice in the matter. And that's a dangerous place because you've lost your autonomy; you've lost your will. And you can gain it back, but it's going to come with sacrifice—it's going to come at a price. You're going to have to separate yourself from alcohol in order to regain yourself, to find physical healing, to reclaim your mental stability. Become informed, become empowered, so that you no longer make alcohol your everything.

- **What if I'm afraid that I won't be accepted by my friends if I quit alcohol?**

True, you probably won't be accepted by the people who continue to drink. They will really have nothing in common with you. If you come around them, if you try to have a connection with them, you guys won't talk the same language anymore. You won't think the same, you won't act the same. And so, they probably will cast you aside. Giving up alcohol will mean changing people, places and things.

You will have to find a new group of people to associate with, a new support system—people who talk recovery, people who talk about not drinking, people who talk about staying sober, getting back on the road of their life, getting back to fulfilling their goals and their dreams. Because alcohol may have robbed them of some time, some dreams, some experiences too.

So yes, you won't really be able to go back to those people, and they may not be accepting of you. And that has to be OK. Yes, it will probably be hurtful. It will probably be life-changing. But if you make the decision that you're going to improve your life, then some relationships will have to go.

- **What if alcohol itself has become my friend and I'm afraid to lose the friendship?**

I've heard that one—and you may have come across it in some other chapters I have written. Alcohol can be your friend. I remember when I was working at the Broadway Center at Johns Hopkins, one of the counselors, Miss Peggy, shared with me that stopping drinking is like losing a friend. I'd never seen it like that. She was much more experienced. And when she said that, I thought, wow, that may really be true. A friend is someone who is there for you when everyone else has left you. Someone who accepts you for who you are, is never going to judge you, is never going to accuse you and is never going to say to you, "Hey, you should stop consuming me."

They're going to say, "Hey, we can be together forever." But what kind of friend would have you consume them or have you be a part of them, knowing they are making your life unmanageable, even destroying it? Knowing they are damaging your relationships and your productivity at work? Your health? I don't consider that a good friend. I consider that a pretty selfish friend. I consider that somebody who only has their own interests in mind—you bought their products, you consumed them, you made them popular, you kept them surviving, you ensured they didn't sit on the shelf and collect dust.

Is that a good friend? They don't seem to have your interests in mind. They don't seem to have your goals in mind. They don't seem to have in mind the things you want to do, the places you want to be, the things you want to accomplish in life, the great person you aspire to be. I don't think that your interest is in their mind at all. So be careful when you say that alcohol is your friend. I'm not sure that's a good friendship.

Your real friends can see what you don't see. They can see you from the outside looking in. And what they see is different from what you see. These are different perspectives. You see yourself one way and other people see you a whole other way. And if you are honest and accept what they say they see, it will give you a better sense of who you are. When I was drinking, a real friend told me I needed to quit alcohol. I wasn't even aware I was performing certain behaviors or talking in certain ways. And my best friend, Adrian, had the wherewithal to capture it on audiotape, because he knew that if he just told me what I had done, I would not have believed him. I would have had a hard time accepting that I had really done those things.

But he grabbed a tape recorder—I'm actually amazed he was able to find a tape recorder, since this was back in the 1980s—and taped it. And so no one had to convince me of what they had seen and heard. I could hear it myself. And I knew that I had changed. I knew that I was not the person who had come in that night before consuming beers and Bacardi rum.

- **What if I am worried because I don't know what my life will look like without alcohol?**

I think it is sometimes challenging for people to know what they will do when they stop drinking. What will your life be like? Right now, alcohol fits into your life. You get your drink in the evening, watch your favorite show and play your songs and music. It is a very pivotal part of your life. So if there are people in your life saying you need to stop drinking—"It will help if you quit drinking, it's going to destroy you, it's going to kill you"—you may be there saying, "What? Drinking is part of my routine. Drinking is what I do." So, you have to find fun elsewhere. You have to find life. You have to find a way to enjoy yourself without alcohol. And that can be scary, especially if you have been a drinker for most of your life. You may have to figure out what to do now without alcohol.

But you're going to open up a new door; you're going to open up a new opportunity for yourself. You're going to open up things that you were blind to in the course of drinking. You need to trust that life without the dysfunction of an alcohol use disorder will be better than living with alcohol. That's part of why giving up drinking takes courage. But trust me— it's better on the other side.

- **Will I experience withdrawal from alcohol?**

Some people do, but not everyone experiences alcohol withdrawals. Sometimes they can be mild, just a case of anxiety, feeling like some impending harm is going to come to you. Sometimes those withdrawals can be severe, with trembling of the body, seizures and even delirium tremens. A lot has to do with how alcohol has affected your nervous system and, when it is removed, how your body copes with its absence.

- **I'm worried about what people will say about me if they find out I have an alcohol use disorder.**

  This is a big one. People might say all kinds of things. They may tell you that you are weak. They may say you are like hell when you drink. But that's as expected, right? I mean, the people who can't handle their drink have lives that are unmanageable and out of order.

  But you don't really have to listen to people who say those things. Because other people will be saying, great for you, more power to you—you have family and children and folks in your corner pushing for you to stay clean, stay sober. It all comes down to who you want to listen to. If you don't want to listen to those people, you escape them. You want to listen to people who are going to be positive, who are going to be in your corner. So you find that group, you find that support. We pick and choose who we want to listen to and what we want to hear.

  We are all human, believe it or not. No matter how skilled we are, how much money we make or how good we look, at the end of the day, we're all human. We all struggle with something; we all have some fights. Remember that anyone who has negative things to say to you about your disorder is fighting their own battles too. They're not perfect either.

- **I am afraid to tell my spiritual leader about my problem with alcohol.**

This can be a challenge sometimes. If you're drinking or using drugs, how can you be honest enough to tell your spiritual leader, to say to your man of God or your woman of God, "Hey, I have a problem"? Are you just living in secret?

There should be someone in the church who is mature enough for you to talk to about your problem. Sometimes that person might be your contact to your recovery, or they might be your window into discovering whether you really have a problem. They might ask you the right questions about your drinking and what kind of impairment or change it is bringing into your life.

And so I encourage you to be honest and not to be in secret, not to try to go about ministry or to go about your walk in the Lord without having that discussion with your spiritual leader. Set up a time to get their evaluation and their take on your drinking. They've got to be honest with you. They are the shepherd for your spiritual life. They're feeding you spiritual food. So, they have to have a sense of where you are, in many aspects of your life, particularly if drinking has become a problem. Make that connection, make that appointment, and see what happens.

- **Will I be accepted by family and friends if I'm sober?**

You won't convince everyone. Maybe your family and friends have seen you go through detox or treatment centers before, and sometimes it annoys people. They think you should get it and not have to keep trying again. Still, they don't understand that addiction is a chronic relapsing disease that has altered and changed the brain, and it has periods of remission, and then it can have moments of relapse.[83]

In all conditions—diabetes, high blood pressure, repetitive stress injuries—people who have gotten their condition under control can return to the behaviors that caused the problem. Relapsing in drinking is the same. The more your family and friends understand the disease of alcohol use, the more accepting they might become.

• **Who will my friends be if I get sober?**

You never know. You never know who's going to be your friend. I think you'll find some really great friends. I think you will find some really remarkable people, people who have struggled like you, people who probably have stories that are worse than your story. But you will never know those people until you have stopped drinking. You'll never get to have those relationships until you cross over to sobriety.

You'll find that there's a world of people who have gone through similar things to you, maybe even worse things, and you'll see how they're coping, how they're functioning, how they really are functioning people—not functioning addicts, but functioning people. You will find people who will be your friends once you seek out sobriety.

If you are a churchgoer, you may find them in the church, even though in church it is kind of taboo to talk about alcohol use disorder or drug addiction. I was with a ministry called the Substance Use Resource and Education Ministry at Dreamlife Worship Center, where people who have struggled with addictions could tune in to Facebook

---

[83] NIDA. 2018, June 6. Understanding Drug Use and Addiction DrugFacts. Retrieved from https://nida.nih.gov/publications/drugfacts/understanding-drug-use-addiction on 2023, June 22.

and learn about ways to get sober. Church can be a great place for people to see freedom from alcohol and drugs, and some members might be very open to discussing how church has helped them in their own recoveries. That said, churches are still places where people might prefer to keep their history of addiction private. Some people open up and tell their story, but some people are reserved and would rather go to an Alcoholics Anonymous meeting and speak about their lives before than share in a church setting. But whether or not church is the place, there are friends you will find who are sober.

- **What's my future if I stop drinking?**

You have a great future. You can now have a clear mind; you are not in a cloud anymore. You can now begin to live everyday life like most Americans. You're not under the influence of a substance. You're not going to have possible withdrawals. You're not becoming someone who people may not know. So, your future looks promising. You can read a whole bunch of stories about people who stopped drinking and how their lives were better off.

Amazingly, some people are very successful while drinking alcohol. And when we see them, we say: "Wow, how could they have so much talent? How could they achieve that?" But they are alcohol users. I think balancing a successful life and drinking is very challenging, and they probably could have been even better without alcohol.

But people are very resilient. They're powerful, they're able to press through, despite their flaws, the things that they go home and struggle with. They're able to come back out and shine in other areas. That's just the resilience of people.

But who you are in the dark should be who you are in the light. And I believe that if you're struggling with anything, including alcohol, you should work to move past it. Your struggles should not limit or hold you back from your complete future and your full potential.

# CHAPTER 11

# How to Stop

There is a way to stop using alcohol and stay stopped. It might sound scary because you tried to stop before but you didn't stay stopped for long, and you returned to the drink, to even more drinking. I'm sorry for that experience in your life. Will you try again? Will you learn from the past so you can stay this time, for your present and future?

• **How does someone quit alcohol?**

Some people just stop—they don't want it anymore. And they just give it up, turn away and never go back. Other people require detoxification; they safely undergo hospitalization and are gradually tapered off alcohol. Some people quit because of their children. They don't want their children to see them under the influence. Some people quit because of a relationship that they want to keep. Some people just find it old and outdated and they've had enough of it.

Some people quit because of the health impact drinking has. Some people quit alcohol because they go to Alcoholics Anonymous and they learn through the testimony of others that they no longer want to drink. And some people just make up their minds. They just say that they've had enough of this—it has taken too much out of them. It is more of a risk than it is a benefit. So, they no longer want to do it.

People take a lot of different approaches. Some people just stop. Other people enter treatment. I would say that medications and behavioral therapy together have been found to be the most effective way to stop drinking alcohol. The top three medications used in therapy are naltrexone or Revia, disulfiram or Antabuse, and acamprosate or Campral. Therapy could mean outpatient therapy or residential therapy, a twenty-eight-day program or a long-term program of six months to twelve months.

When you stop alcohol, you do need the medicines to help the body to feel better. But you also need information and education, so that you can get a new way of thinking. And some of that treatment involves family therapy, because family dysfunction is often associated with drinking.

But the first step is to come into a place where you find that your consequences from drinking outweigh your benefit. You're not enjoying the drink, and you're only drinking because you don't want to feel bad with the withdrawal.

And then afterward, you can participate in Alcoholics Anonymous, a good support system. You may find refuge in your church or other spiritual setting. You may be able to get your family into support groups too, like Al-Anon or Alateen.

That is how you quit.

• **Why is it so hard to get sober and maintain sobriety?**

That can vary. Some people say it's hard to get sober because so many people drink. It's hard to maintain it because alcohol is so plentiful, with bars everywhere. But I think those are just excuses. I don't think it's hard to get sober if you put forth the effort. We have a saying, "stick and stay"—stay with it, stay committed. Find yourself in the right place. Get yourself a plan. Have accountability, people you answer to, to maintain sobriety, and over time you'll get stronger in your sobriety and stronger in your ability to say no.

And of course, you might have a slip, you might revert to your old ways, but you can get yourself back up and get connected. Some people get a sponsor—someone they are accountable to who helps them in working through The Big Book, which is an integral part of the Alcoholics Anonymous movement. They keep themselves connected, they keep themselves involved, and they find themselves enjoying life again. They find some kind of fulfillment that helps them maintain their sobriety.

- **I have given up on trying to stop drinking because I feel like a failure over and over again.**

You're asking what's the use of trying to stop. You feel like a failure. But maybe deep down, you just aren't ready to give up alcohol. I've met people who won't stop drinking; some have said that they like to drink and use drugs. They are not ready to stop. They don't want to stop. The consequences of their actions haven't been that bad. They haven't gone to jail. They haven't sold their bodies. They haven't had any real health challenges. They may or may not be going to the doctor, either.

And so, they may have given up trying to stop drinking because, over and over again, it just hasn't worked for them. After all, deep down inside, they don't want to stop. They like the taste of alcohol. They like the effect of alcohol. As the Luther Ingram song says, "If loving you is wrong, I don't want to be right."

I would encourage you to give it another try. Recovery is about trying again and again until you get it right. We say in the treatment world, "Keep coming back—it works if you work it." It's seldom a one-time try and cure. Sometimes it is, but most of the time it's persistence that brings huge rewards.

- **Who should I tell that I think I have a drinking problem?**

You can tell the people who are close to you. You can tell your medical doctor. You can tell somebody who cares. Because if you're telling them that you have a problem, I hope that you're telling them because you're asking for help. You're not just saying, "Hey, I've got this situation." You're saying it because you want support for it. And if someone cares, they'll call and try to get you the help you need.

- **How and why do addiction nurses treat alcohol use disorder?**

Above all, addiction nurses treat AUDs because they care.

When I was taking a class at Dundalk, the teacher said something that followed me. He said that in this profession, you want to be caring and you want to be knowledgeable. You could be caring, but if you don't have the right information for people, you can't help them. And if you're knowledgeable but don't care, that won't help them either, because then they won't trust you. But when you combine a caring nurse and a knowledgeable nurse, that person will do some great work.

An addiction nurse knows a lot about alcohol use disorder. They know how to respond to a patient who is sharing information. They know how to be caring, empathetic and understanding that a patient may need encouragement and some inspiration—and then they know how to assess and see where there may be possible influence.

They know how to use a breathalyzer, how to take an individual's vital signs and how to advocate for the individual and with the doctors and the counselors regarding treatment. They know about the medicines and their side effects, how to educate the patient about how the medicines work and how to explain that the patient must go to groups and follow what the counselors advise them to do.

They know something about AA. They are learning about Alcoholics Anonymous, Al-Anon and Alateen. They are able to help the patient along their journey, work with that counselor, work with that doctor, not taking the supreme attitude that they know everything but knowing that they are part of a team.

Treatment nurses like me are trying to get you sober and get your family well-connected so they can love you and be the best family and support you can ever have.

- **What is the job of an addiction treatment counselor?**

A counselor plays a very pivotal role. They spend a lot of time with patients. They want to develop rapport. They want to make sure the patient is able to trust them. And they want to instill some tools, some coping skills and some strategies that will keep the patient from craving or relapsing, helping them to understand the disease of addiction and to navigate the road of recovery.

The counselor helps the patient develop a treatment plan, not telling the patient what they ought to do but allowing them to find the system that will work for them. The counselor doesn't tell the patient what to do but helps them accomplish the goals they have set. And so, a counselor is a very pivotal part of the team. They're like the quarterback who helps and guides and cares for that patient in treatment.

- **Is Alcoholics Anonymous right for me?**

I once had a guest on my Facebook Live show, Dr. Michael Hayes, who shared that Alcoholics Anonymous is a great tool to help people maintain sobriety. AA started in 1935, two years after alcohol was legalized,[84] and it has continued to be an excellent resource for people who want to be sober. People who are no longer drinking share their testimony, and their testimony encourages and inspires and lets people know that they're not alone and that they, too, can overcome the disease of alcohol use.

And so, I would encourage you to go to an Alcoholics Anonymous meeting. If you're not comfortable in your area, you can always seek out ones much farther away. We do have some virtual Alcoholics Anonymous meetings, where you can even hide your face and change your name, and still be a part of the meeting and get that information and testimony. You can learn from other people's experiences. You don't have to experience everything yourself. But if you learn from what someone else shared, it can still have an impact on you. The

---

[84] Alcoholics Anonymous (1, January 1). The Start and Growth of A.A. https://www.aa.org/the-start-and-growth-of-aa. Retrieved September 21, 2023, from https://www.aa.org/the-start-and-growth-of-aa#:~:text=A.A.%20began%20in%201935%20in,Both%20had%20been%20hopeless%20alcoholics.

course of your behavior may change, and what you decide to do.

- **How does a doctor treat a person with an alcohol use disorder?**

Doctors do incredible work with people who have an alcohol use disorder. They start by assessing how severe this AUD is.

Some things a doctor can do are be empathetic, be knowledgeable about the disease, and help you and your family recover from an alcohol use disorder. They may recommend outpatient treatment, attending meetings, and engaging in family therapy, and they may even suggest mental health treatment because a good proportion of people who have a substance use disorder have a mental illness as well.

Do you need medications to assist in your recovery? The doctor will prescribe medications, benzodiazepines, to see that you safely transition from alcohol. One of the leading medications we use today to help with alcohol cravings is naltrexone. We sometimes use the injectable form, Vivitrol, which you take once a month. If you are a severe alcohol user and know that you're likely going to drink, we offer Antabuse or disulfiram because you will get sick and have immediate consequences from drinking. If you have liver damage already, another medicine we can use is Campral, which will help with alcohol cravings as well. So, in addition to all the other help they provide, a doctor may prescribe those things for you.

• **Can praying to my higher power take alcohol away from me?**

Absolutely. You can pray; you can believe your spiritual source of power to be a force that can take the taste for alcohol away, take the drive to drink away. I am a strong believer that God or your spiritual higher power can take the taste for alcohol away and the desire for alcohol, depending on your faith and what you believe. But if it doesn't happen, you can't say that your higher power failed and so you must return to drinking.

Sometimes people get in their minds, "Well, if God didn't want me to do it, he'd take it away from me." If this is you, you have to find another strategy. You have to find something else in addition to praying about it to help you stop. You can't make the excuse that "Well, God didn't take it away. I prayed. So, I'm just going to have to go back to drinking." That's unacceptable. Your higher power may just want you to do whatever it takes and to explore all the different means to find your recovery and your sobriety.

• **What are some common encouraging words that can help me maintain sobriety?**

In treatment, we say, "don't give up." Come to your meetings, go to your appointments, stick and stay. Make the decision that you know you're not going anywhere, you're not going to be turned, you're not going to be moved in a direction that will keep you from getting the most out of your recovery program.

What does it mean when we say "one day at a time"? This phrase used in the treatment world means that your recovery from alcohol is one day at a time. It's a reminder not to think ahead to the future and say, "Oh, I hope to be clean January 14, because that's my birthday," or "I hope to be clean February 8, because that's when my daughter gets married."

But take it one day at a time. Look at today. You're clean just for the day. That helps you not put a bunch of anxiety on yourself, but relish the day, just make the most of the day, do all that you're supposed to do today. Because you're sober just for the day. You didn't take a drink. You went to a meeting. You might have had some stress. You might have had some problems. Some issues popped up. But you found a way to work it all out for the day.

And so, "one day at a time" is a pivotal way of thinking. I learned the importance of one day at a time through COVID. Knowing that lives were lost and people were changed forever by a viral infection, I made up my mind that each day I was given was the day I would celebrate.

The Scripture talks about this concept. It says, "This is the day the Lord has made; we will rejoice and be glad in it" (Psalms 118:24). God did so much to make this day. The most I can do is rejoice and be happy in the day. And so, it has great significance for you who are recovering from alcohol. Take the day, just to enjoy the day, and make the most of it. And think of each day like that. And you'll see yourself with days and weeks and months and years of recovery, just for the day.

- **Can I just decrease my drinking if I am a heavy drinker?**

Some people try this. Some say, "Well, I don't drink as much as I used to. I drink less." But I think if you were a severe or heavy drinker, you have to be an abstinent drinker.

I don't think there is lighter drinking for you. You may rationalize in your mind that you're drinking less, but are you certain that you're consuming less?

I think you should have nothing to do with it. It needs to be your past; you must remove yourself from it. I'm expressing my feelings here, just giving my thoughts on the matter. I think you have to have nothing to do with alcohol.

- **What if I slip? What's the difference between that and a relapse?**

Sometimes, someone will pick up a drink and drink it, then realize it wasn't good and put it down, or maybe someone gave them something they didn't know about. These are slips. People can slip and not entirely fall.

A slip does not have to turn into a relapse if you stop yourself before you abandon your recovery. If you give up on your recovery and return to drinking regularly, this is considered relapsing, which can be more difficult to stop.[85]

But I do think if you recognize it, and you get yourself right to a meeting, reach out to your sponsor or jump right in there and get back on track, we can call that a slip, not a complete relapse. It all depends on who you talk to. But I would say the important thing is that you got back up, you got on the road, even if you call it a relapse. You understand this is a disease of a chronic nature and remissions and relapses are part of the process.

---

[85] Pyramid Healthcare, Inc. (2017, November 14). Slip vs Relapse: What's the Difference? https://www.Pyramid-Healthcare.com. Retrieved September 21, 2023, from https://www.pyramid-healthcare.com/slip-versus-relapse/#:~:text=A%20slip%20does%20not%20have,be%20more%20difficult%20to%20stop.

- **Will I ever be forgiven for the wrongs that my drinking has caused?**

Hopefully, people will forgive you; hopefully, you'll demonstrate you can be trusted. But people are strange. Sometimes they'll forgive you. Sometimes they won't. And you can do nothing about it except continue to have love in your heart toward them. You don't know the pain that your drinking caused them. And as much as you try and try, it may not be the same to them as it is to you. You have to be accepting of that.

- **Can I forgive myself for the things I've done due to my drinking?**

I believe you can work through the process of forgiving yourself. You may need the assistance of a trained therapist, spiritual leader or sponsor—someone who has had recovery from alcohol for some years and can guide you through important principles and the Alcoholics Anonymous curriculum. Just be willing to do the work. Your AUD didn't develop overnight; it won't be fixed overnight. Be patient with yourself and always keep people around you who can see you from the outside. Sometimes you can't see what other people see about you, so it's important to have that outside perspective.

- **What do I tell someone who wants to try alcohol?**

From your experience, you should tell them: "Don't do it. Don't try it. Don't get accustomed to it. Don't get used to the taste of it or the feeling of it. Just stay away. Find something else to do with your life. Find something else fun and enjoyable to do. Just don't explore it." That's what I would say.

But people will be curious. They say when you tell someone no, that's what they will do. So, let me give you the example of what I tell my son. He's very daring and courageous, and he'll try most things to get the attention and the wow from the crowd. So I say to him that I pray he doesn't have an awful experience with alcohol if he does choose to try it. I tell him I can't be sure that he won't use it, even though his dad is an addiction treatment nurse. But I say I pray that it won't bring him a lot of harm. And hopefully, if he does try it, he'll have the kind of consequence that will make him equate drinking with a bad thing that happened—something that didn't destroy him, but it wasn't good. And he won't want to drink anymore.

It's like what happened with me with cigarettes—I smoked, I got dizzy, my sisters caught me and I got in trouble, so immediately I realized cigarettes weren't suitable. I had so many consequences all at one time.

So what should you tell someone who wants to try alcohol? You tell them your experience; you just tell them what it was like for you.

• **Is it acceptable to go to addiction conferences and socially drink?**

I don't think so. I've attended some addiction conferences and seen people drinking alcohol at the meeting. And to me, I think it is a kind of a slap in the face for us to have wine and all these things. We're teaching about addiction. We're teaching about not drinking and drugging. I think those substances don't need to be there. But that's just my take and my feelings.

- **Will you tell the world about alcohol, Joseph?**

Yes, I will tell the world about alcohol. I saw alcohol, and I saw what it did to my family and how it had a bearing and an impact on us. And I don't want it to affect your family. If someone in your family is having trouble with alcohol, I want you to be able to go to support groups like Al-Anon and Alateen. And I want the people in your family to be able to turn away, to turn down alcohol, to put it down, just like my mom one day decided to put it down and never pick it up again.

I want them to be able to go to their place of worship. I want them to find support groups to help them understand the disease of alcohol use disorder. I want the one who's suffering from AUD to know that there is help, that treatment is available, that there are programs, there are open doors for them, they can get the help they need, they can get the sobriety they need and get the life they need.

And so, to do that, I have to tell the world. I have to write books and make videos. I have to do as much as I can to tell the whole world that there is a life outside of alcohol. You can find fun, you can find enjoyment, you can find a new way of living life and you can change the way you live. You don't have to have your life cut short because of an alcohol use disorder.

- **Can I become a spokesperson against the dangers of alcohol?**

Absolutely. People do it all the time. You could be a spokesperson on Facebook, on YouTube, elsewhere on social media or by writing books.

If you experienced the harms of alcohol or you saw someone else experience them and you have an ache, you have anger, you're mad about what alcohol did and you don't want it to do that to anyone else, those are good ingredients to make you a spokesperson. It's not just for the limelight but because you want to see someone's life change. You don't want to see someone suffer as you or others suffered. So, be a spokesperson. Pull out your phone and make videos. Get out your pen and paper, get out your tape recorder, and start writing what you feel. You'll be out there fighting against a great enemy.

Yes, alcohol brings in a lot of money, substantial revenue streams. There are famous people promoting it. But, hey, guess what? You're not fighting alone. It was just two years after alcohol was approved in 1933 that Alcoholics Anonymous came forth. And the fight has been going on since then.

We've been fighting for quite a while, and we're not going to stop fighting, because we know people suffer. People die. And if no one is making the noise, then all those bottles have won. But all those bottles have not succeeded, because some people, like me and you, are going to stand and make some noise and try to get someone changed, one day at a time.

Printed in Great Britain
by Amazon

43340340R00076